ANTS

ANTS

A VISUAL GUIDE

HEATHER CAMPBELL AND BENJAMIN BLANCHARD

PRINCETON UNIVERSITY PRESS
PRINCETON AND OXFORD

Published in 2023 by Princeton University Press
41 William Street, Princeton, New Jersey 08540
99 Banbury Road, Oxford OX2 6JX
press.princeton.edu

Library of Congress Control Number 2022940432
British Library Cataloging-in-Publication Data is available

ISBN: 978-0-691-22852-5

This book was conceived, designed, and produced by
The Bright Press, an imprint of the Quarto Group,
The Old Brewery, 6 Blundell Street,
London N7 9BH, United Kingdom.
T (0)20 7700 6700
www.quarto.com

The Bright Press
PUBLISHER: James Evans
EDITORIAL DIRECTOR: Isheeta Mustafi
ART DIRECTOR: James Lawrence
MANAGING EDITOR: Jacqui Sayers
PROJECT EDITORS: Joanna Bentley, Anna Southgate
DESIGN: Kevin Knight
PICTURE RESEARCH: Jane Smith

Cover images: (front) Adisak Mitrprayoon/istock;
(spine) Simon Dannhauer/Shutterstock
Cover design by: Kevin Knight

Typeset in: Chaparral Pro

Printed and bound in Singapore

10 9 8 7 6 5 4 3 2 1

CONTENTS

INTRODUCING THE ANTS

THE HUMBLE ANT IS HARDWORKING, UBIQUITOUS, and instantly recognizable to people across the globe. From city sidewalk to rainforest canopy, we cross paths with ants, yet we rarely consider what has made them so successful that they occupy virtually every nook and cranny of land on Earth. Ants can make up one-third of insect biomass, an amount many times greater than all terrestrial vertebrates. A single colony of Leafcutter Ants has more individuals than the entire population of New York City (10 million ants vs. 8.6 million people). But profusion alone does not define their importance; rather, it is their essential roles in ecosystems and their vast host of interactions with other organisms. Take the Army Ant *Eciton burchellii* as an example; this single species is associated with at least 557 other species, including over 200 birds.

Their relationships with other species cover a vast range of interactions—from tightly coevolved mutualisms nesting in specialized plant structures, to their role tending sap-sucking bugs. They are voracious predators renowned for their strength and ability to take down prey much larger than themselves using chemical weapons alongside impressive jaws and even more impressive stings. Ants host a range of visitors in their nests, from other invertebrates to fungi that they cultivate for food. Some creatures, such as spiders, mimic them hoping to gain a benefit from appearing to be an aggressive or unpalatable ant.

As a group, the Formicidae—better known as ants— are a family that sits within the larger insect order of Hymenoptera, which includes bees, sawflies, and wasps. We know of around 14,000 ant species, but estimates add potentially another 10,000 species not yet discovered or described by taxonomists. Belonging to a single family of insects, ants are subdivided into 16 living subfamilies with

LEFT: A widespread ant–insect mutualism is the tending of phloem-feeding hemipterans, which produce sugary honeydew. The ants feed on this and in return provide protection against predator and parasitoid attack for the bugs.

OPPOSITE TOP: The possession of elaborate spines is part of an evolutionary trade-off against other ant defensive traits, such as having a functional sting.

OPPOSITE BOTTOM: Worker ants, such as these *Leptogenys*, will move eggs, larvae, and pupae within a nest and to new nest sites.

an additional 6 subfamilies that contain only extinct species. Diversity is highly variable across subfamily groups: some contain a single species while the hugely successful Myrmicinae subfamily has over 7,000 species.

While it is easy enough to point out an ant when we see one, it is harder to pinpoint what exactly makes it an ant. Ants are characterized by modified abdominal waist segments, elbowed antennae, and a metapleural gland. More recognizable is the lack of winged individuals in the worker caste, which sets them apart from many of their nearest bee and wasp relatives. By eye they generally appear to be dark six-legged specks that are fairly hard to tell apart while busily scurrying around. Under a microscope they are revealed to have huge variation in their appearance, with features such as scythe-like snapping jaws, ostentatious spikes, bizarrely shaped hairs, or large glitter ball eyes.

We find ourselves fascinated by ant societies—female-led colonies where members work cooperatively to find food and raise young. Colonies may contain a few individuals up to a million, depending on the species. Colonies have one or more queens, with daughter workers who forage for food and take care of the young within the nest. Effectively this means that all workers are closely related as sisters. Queens can be long-lived (up to 30 years in one species), in contrast to males, who are generally short-lived, existing only long enough to

mate with a queen. In true ant style, this insect has developed many variations on this basic life history. Some species have reproductive workers instead of a queen caste, while others live parasitically inside the nest of host species.

Their behaviors are perhaps the thing that amazes us most about ants: They have a remarkable ability to cooperate and communicate to defend their nest from intruders or to collectively hunt and bring back food to their nest. The reproductive capacity of a queen ant sees her producing over 250 million eggs in a lifetime. And a queen is capable of invading the nest of another species, killing the original queen, and then manipulating the remaining workers of an entirely different species to feed and raise her young for her. We even know of ants who rescue their injured nestmates and act as ambulances, carrying the injured back to the nest to rest and recuperate. All of these amazing facets of ant behavior, alongside their interactions, anatomy, and life history, are covered in this book.

ANT CLASSIFICATION CHART

Phylum: Arthropoda | Class: Insecta | Order: Hymenoptera | Family: Formicidae

Subfamilies	Diversity	Notes
The "Big Five"		
Dolichoderinae	28 genera, 714 species (136 species)	Single petiole and slit-like orifice used for chemical defense. Most speciose genera are *Dolichoderus*, *Technomyrmex*, *Azteca*, and *Iridomyrmex*.
Dorylinae	27 genera, 749 species (8 species)	Robust sting. Most speciose genera are *Aenictus*, *Neivamyrmex*, and *Lioponera*.
Formicinae	52 genera, 3,244 species (171 species)	This subfamily contains 23 percent of the world's ant species. Single petiole and acidopore. Over a thousand species are *Camponotus*.
Myrmicinae	147 genera, 7,075 species (187 species)	Over half of the world's species are in this subfamily. Petiole and postpetiole nodes. *Pheidole*, *Strumigenys*, and *Tetramorium* are most speciose genera.
Ponerinae	50 genera, 1,267 species (87 species)	Single petiole segment and usually a robust sting. Most diverse genera are *Leptogenys*, *Hypoponera*, and *Anochetus*.
Smaller Subfamilies		
Agroecomyrmecinae	2 genera, 2 species (3 species)	2 living species, *Ankylomyrma coronacantha* and *Tatuidris tatusia*
Amblyoponinae	9 genera, 143 species (7 species)	Highest diversity in *Fulakora*, *Stigmatomma*, and *Prionopelta*
Aneuretinae	1 genus, 1 species (12 species)	Single living species, *Aneuretus simoni*, from Sri Lanka
Apomyrminae	1 genus, 1 species	1 species, *Apomyrma stygia*, from West Africa
Ectatomminae	12 genera, 302 species (14 species)	Most diverse genera are *Gnamptogenys* and *Rhytidoponera*
Leptanillinae	7 genera, 70 species	Most diverse genus is *Leptanilla*
Martialinae	1 genus, 1 species	1 species, *Martialis heureka*, from Brazil
Myrmeciinae	2 genera, 94 species (22 species)	All living species are in *Myrmecia* (93 spp.) except 1 species in *Nothomyrmecia*
Paraponerinae	1 genus, 1 species (1 species)	1 living species, *Paraponera clavata*, and 1 fossil species, *Paraponera dieteri*
Proceratiinae	3 genera, 165 species (12 species)	3 genera are *Proceratium*, *Discothyrea*, and *Probolomyrmex*
Pseudomyrmecinae	3 genera, 235 species (20 species)	3 genera are *Pseudomyrmex*, *Tetraponera*, and the single-species genus *Myrcidris*

Subfamilies	Diversity	Notes
Known only from fossils		
Armaniinae	2 genera, 12 species	Genera are *Armania* and *Pseudarmania*
Brownimeciinae	1 genus, 1 species	Monotypic genus with 1 species, *Brownimecia clavata*
Formiciinae	2 genera, 6 species	Genera are *Formicium* and *Titanomyrma*
Haidomyrmecinae	10 genera, 16 species	All genera have 1 species except for *Ceratomyrmex* (2 spp.), *Haidomyrmex* (4 spp.), and *Linguamyrmex* (3 spp.)
Sphecomyrminae	4 genera, 12 species	*Gerontoformica* is the most diverse genus (9 species)
Zigrasimeciinae	3 genera, 6 species	Genera are *Boltonimecia* (1 sp.), *Protozigrasimecia* (1 sp.), and *Zigrasimecia* (4 spp.)

Figures listed give only the extant diversity within a subfamily. Figures in parentheses give the additional diversity for extinct species. The diversity within subfamilies known only from fossils are all extinct genera and species.

WHO STUDIES ANTS?

Scientists who specialize in conducting research on ant biology are known as myrmecologists, with the field of ant biology itself referred to as myrmecology (from the Greek *myrmex* for ants). As well as natural scientists who study many aspects of the biology of ants, computer scientists and engineers also study these insects. Research hubs exist in the USA, Brazil, Germany, Australia, France, Japan, China, and the UK. As with many subdisciplines of entomology, tropical regions are generally less well characterized in terms of their ant fauna even though they have the greatest species diversity. This is changing, but requires investment in ant research for countries in the Global South. Traditionally, European and American men have been credited as pioneers in myrmecology with contributions from women and scientists from other countries often being overlooked. Currently, women represent around one third of authors publishing research on ants, and data is not available on the proportion of scientists from other marginalized groups. While participation is increasing, there is still a long way to go to create a truly diverse and equitable community of myrmecologists.

ABOVE: Within a nest, adult worker ants are found alongside a queen as well as juvenile stages of the colony known as the brood (eggs, larvae, and pupae).

ANT ENVIRONMENTS

Ants are found in all parts of the globe except the coldest polar regions and some islands. Throughout the book we use eight broad biogeographic regions to describe the distributions of different species. The Neotropical realm includes Central and South America as well as the Caribbean, with the Nearctic covering most of North America. The vast Palearctic region comprises Europe, Asia from north of the Himalayas, and Africa northwards of the Sahara. The Holarctic is sometimes used to collectively refer to a Northern Hemisphere distribution of ants that combines the Nearctic and Palearctic regions. The Afrotropical realm includes Africa south of the Sahara, parts of the Arabian Peninsula, and the island of Madagascar. The Indomalayan region is made up of India and Southeast Asia, while Australasia includes Australia, New Guinea, and the eastern part of Indonesia.

Oceania includes Micronesia, Fijian islands, Hawaiian islands, and Polynesia. The final zone, the Antarctic, is not occupied by ants. Across all regions most terrestrial habitats are occupied by ants. These can include natural and semi-natural forest, woodland, grassland, scrub, wetland, and desert areas. Ants frequently occupy human-modified areas, such as agricultural land used for crops, livestock pasture and forest plantations, or urban spaces.

BELOW: Ants are adapted to nesting in many microhabitats above and below ground. They are especially influenced by the availability and structure of live and dead vegetation.

OPPOSITE: The seven biogeographic realms that are used throughout this book when describing the distribution patterns of ants (Antarctica excluded).

ANT NESTING SITES

Woven from leaves

Ant garden from plant material and epiphytic plants

Excavated live wood

Under logs or inside rotting/ hollow logs

Mound building

In soil under stones

The majority of ants occupy a nest or series of nests where the colony lives, providing safe and stable conditions for the queen and brood, as well as a central point from which workers forage for food. Other ants have a nomadic lifestyle, foraging and nesting on the move, and sometimes constructing bivouac shelters weaved from their own bodies.

Ants broadly fall into two nesting categories: ground or arboreal. Ground-nesting ants have a host of options. They may be subterranean, excavating their own nests deep within the soil; live in leaf-litter; or nest opportunistically under rocks and logs. Ground-nesting ants make use of plant material even when they do not directly occupy trees. They will nest in cavities such as hollow dead branches and twigs, or inside nuts and seeds on the forest floor, and especially inside rotting logs.

Arboreal ants nest on or in trees, exploiting a host of strategies. Some ants can tunnel into live wood, creating their own holes to nest in or excavating a network of galleries under bark. Others are able to weave together leaves to construct a nest or create ant gardens, a creation that combines recycled plant material with epiphytic plant seeds sown in for structural integrity. Plants may provide domatia, specialized modified structures like swollen thorns or hollow branch segments that are specifically grown for ant occupation.

Ants often show a specialization to a particular foraging or nesting stratum (subterranean, leaf litter, canopy) but are not strictly limited to foraging in the same microhabitat that they nest in. Many arboreal nesting ants will forage on the ground, while ground-nesting ants move on to trees to hunt or find plant-based resources like nectar or honeydew from insects.

MAP OF BIOGEOGRAPHIC REALMS

Nearctic

Palearctic

Division of the biogeographic realms approximately follows the red dashed lines.

Afrotropical

Indomalayan

Oceanian

Neotropical

Australasian

Areas shaded green are known to contain high species diversity that is generally concentrated in tropical forests.

ABOUT THIS BOOK

This book contains six chapters covering different aspects of the biology and ecology of ants. While many topics are intertwined, this organization allows us to explore major themes in the natural history of ants. Accompanying the topic chapters are profiles of ant genera that highlight the unique stories of the featured groups.

TOPIC CHAPTERS

What is an Ant? offers an overview of the physical features of ants, including their basic body plan. We examine details of external anatomy, including morphology used in attack and defense, as well as structures used for locomotion and sensing the environment. We also look at the internal systems of ants and outline their reproductive anatomy.

Evolution and Diversity summarizes ant evolution and examines in turn each of the "Big Five" most diverse ant subfamilies. We look at theories explaining ant dominance, and the innovations and trade-offs that have contributed to their success. The fossil record for ants is discussed, and then we highlight the global distribution patterns of ant diversity, especially ants found on islands.

Life History, Reproduction, and Development gives an insight into the ant life cycle, including how and when mating occurs. Colony foundation occurs in many ways for ants, and these are discussed followed by the process of sex determination. Eusociality and the different castes of ants are outlined, with a discussion on exploitation of workers.

Behavior begins by introducing how ants navigate and forage and goes on to outline the varying methods of ant communication. There then follows a description of the ant "social stomach" and trophallaxis, followed by a review of other diverse behaviors, including the use of vision, aggression, defense, nest construction, and memory.

Ecology undertakes a review of the main topics in ant ecology—an area with a substantial amount of scientific research. We begin by examining direct and indirect competitive ant interactions and how these relate to ant coexistence and niche partitioning. We then look at a range of ant interactions with other organisms such as mutualisms, commensalisms, and antagonistic interactions with predators and parasites. Finally, we briefly cover the impact of human-induced habitat loss and routes of ant species conservation.

Ants and People shows how ants touch human lives in diverse ways, for example through their role in agriculture, their use as food and pharmaceuticals, and the cultural value of ants in art and storytelling. We end by describing how the public has been involved in ant research through citizen science and the global impacts of invasive ant species.

ANT PROFILES

The ant profiles are an opportunity to delve deeper into the biology of a particular group. These are typically presented at the level of genus, with the exception of the fossil group of Hell Ants, which are a subfamily. Common names are also given where they exist, although many ants do not have them, and other genera share a common name. Each profile gives a brief overview of the biology and ecology before focusing on interesting features of the taxon. Due to ants' small size and cryptic lifestyles, many aspects of their biology are not well understood, but the detail in these profiles gives some glimpse into what we currently know about them. Information on distributions, habitats occupied, and feeding and nesting preferences are given to the best of current scientific knowledge.

OPPOSITE: Among the topics discussed are (clockwise from top left) external ant anatomy; morphological traits; communication; impact on the environment; interactions in the natural world; and colony migration.

1 | WHAT IS AN ANT?

ANT ANATOMY

ANTS CAN BE CHARACTERIZED BY a combination of three unique physical features: a distinct one- or two-segmented waist, elbowed antennae, and a metapleural gland. They follow a basic insect body plan. This includes six legs, two pairs of wings (which are absent in workers), and division into three main body sections. As invertebrates they have no spine or internal skeleton, instead relying on a hard, waterproof exoskeleton made of chitin to give their body rigidity and protection. The exoskeleton is punctuated with spiracles, small breathing holes that allow the uptake of oxygen into the body. Beyond this superficially simple anatomical outline, ants exhibit a wondrous range of physical adaptations. It is this specialization of form and function that has allowed ants to flourish in virtually every terrestrial habitat on Earth.

BODY PLAN

Insects have three body regions: the head, thorax, and abdomen, whereas ants have differently named sections: the head, mesosoma, and gaster. The mesosoma is the middle body section, formed as the first abdominal segment (the propodeum) is fused to the thorax. The next one or two abdominal segments are much reduced in size to become small nodes. They form a distinctive waist known as the petiole and (if present) postpetiole, which is a defining characteristic of ants. These waist segments are useful to prevent misidentification where ants might be confused with small wasps or the erroneously named Velvet Ants, which are not in fact ants at all. The first step in identifying an ant to subfamily is to count the number of waist segments. Subfamilies including the Dolichoderinae, Formicinae, and Ponerinae have one waist segment, while the Myrmicinae and Pseudomyrmecinae have two waist segments. Following the petiolar nodes is the gaster, composed of the remaining abdominal segments.

MESOSOMA

The size of the mesosoma relative to the rest of the body is a good indicator of whether an ant will have wings and fly at any stage of its life cycle. In the case of males and reproductive females, queens, the thorax is enlarged to allow space for the flight muscles. Where present, ants possess two pairs of membranous wings. Wingless ants may be queens who have lost their wings after use—who are dealate. Alternatively, they may be female workers who never possess them to begin with. They are generally easy to tell apart as dealate queens are larger than workers and possess wing scars where wings have been bitten or rubbed off.

GASTER

When it comes to organs, the ant brain and associated nervous system, along with the heart, run longitudinally through the mesosoma and gaster. Within the gaster, ants house their digestive and reproductive organs. They have two stomachs, one for their own digestion and the other a social stomach for sharing food in the colony. At the tip of the gaster, external evidence of defensive structures can be seen. Depending on the ant subfamily, they may possess a sting, a formic acid–spraying funnel of hairs known as an acidopore, or a simple slit. A unique identifying character of ants is the presence of the metapleural gland, although it has been lost in some subfamilies. This slit or round-shaped opening in the exoskeleton is a secretory gland found at the base of the propodeum. Its full significance is not understood. It could be for odor recognition or territorial marking but is most likely used in sanitation and chemical defense.

All the structures mentioned in this overview are elaborated on in the sections that follow. The different subfamilies are treated in more detail in Chapter 2.

ANT ANATOMY

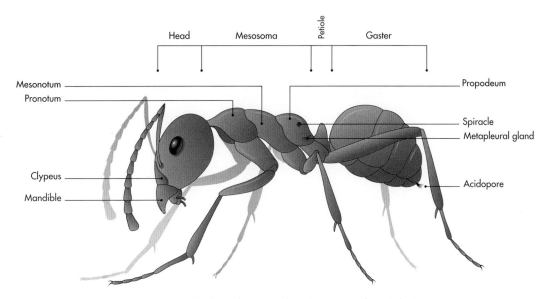

Head | Mesosoma | Petiole | Gaster

Mesonotum
Pronotum
Clypeus
Mandible

Propodeum
Spiracle
Metapleural gland
Acidopore

ABOVE: As shown here a single waist segment, the petiole, is typical of subfamilies including the Dolichoderinae, Formicinae, and Ponerinae. Another notable feature includes the presence of a metapleural gland, a unique structure found only in ants.

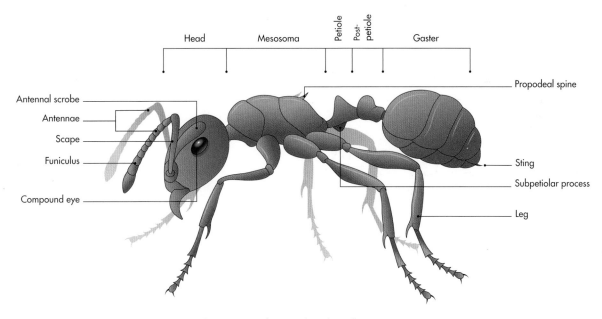

Head | Mesosoma | Petiole | Post-petiole | Gaster

Antennal scrobe
Antennae
Scape
Funiculus
Compound eye

Propodeal spine
Sting
Subpetiolar process
Leg

ABOVE: The presence of antennal scrobes allows an ant to retract its antennae to be flush with its face. The two-segmented waist, comprised of a petiole and postpetiole, is indicative of ants belonging to subfamilies such as the Myrmicinae and Pseudomyrmecinae.

WHEN FORM MEETS FUNCTION

MANY ASPECTS OF AN ANT'S appearance have likely evolved to meet a specific lifestyle requirement, although the extent to which this is true has not been fully explored for all aspects of anatomy. Adaptations could be due to environment, available food, or predators. Long legs and large eyes are commonly seen in ground-foraging ants that need to move quickly to avoid predators in open ground or be the first to acquire a food resource. In contrast, ants that forage and nest in leaf litter have shorter legs and antennae, alongside small eyes. This makes sense in the dark environment of leaf litter where moving through small spaces is easier with a compact body plan. Based on the unique combination of body size measurements, scientists can predict where an ant nests and forages or even what kind of food it eats. Predators have longer, flatter mandibles, while omnivores—those eating a diverse range of foods—have shorter, curved mandibles.

Size and shape alone are not the only ways in which ants vary in appearance. After seeing them under a microscope, the idea of ants as uniform specks of red or black quickly evaporates. While they may not compare with the gaudy splendor of multicolored butterfly wings, they do exhibit a range of hues in blacks, browns, reds, oranges, and yellows.

Australia is home to ants in an even wider array of colors: *Rhytidoponera metallica* is more commonly known as the Green-Headed Ant for its green-blue metallic appearance, while ants in the genus *Iridomyrmex,* meaning Rainbow Ant, often possess blue, green, or purple iridescence. The most dazzling of all ants are those covered in a fine layer of golden hairs, such as the spectacular Golden Carpenter Ant, *Camponotus sericeiventris*, found in forests across Central and South America.

The thick cuticle that forms the ant exoskeleton can be highly patterned and covered in hairs. In fact, the terminology alone to describe "sculpturation"—the depressions and ridges of the cuticle—requires a 31-page guide. Ants range from having unsculptured, smooth, or glossy surfaces free of marks, to superficial wrinkles and bumps, through to deep corrugations and dense punctuations. The surface landscape of an ant sees sculpturing combined with "pilosity," the density of rigid hairs (setae) on the body, and "pubescence," the shorter fine hairs elsewhere. Hairs on ants come in many different shapes, including clavate (club-shaped), ovate (egg-shaped), reniform (kidney-shaped), and spatulate (spatula-shaped). Specialized hairs may help defend ants against predators, while certain

BELOW: Known commonly as Meat Ants, *Iridomyrmex purpureus* have an orange-to-red head and mesosoma with strong iridescence visible on their gaster.

BELOW: *Calyptomyrmex piripilis* is found across the Afrotropics from Sudan to South Africa. It has small eyes and characteristic scale-shaped hairs of unknown function.

patterns of sculpturing can create a stronger cuticle, another line of defense. Being hairy and having a thicker, more sculptured cuticle can also help avoid desiccation through water loss. It is even likely that these properties assist in thermoregulation, as hair thickness and reflectivity may help control body temperature and provide UV resistance.

LEFT: The widespread Australian genus *Rhytidoponera* exhibits a range of metallic colors from green and blue through purple.

BELOW LEFT: Arboreal *Cataulacus* ants have thick, highly sculptured exoskeletons, often with protective teeth or spines on their thorax and propodeum.

BELOW: Found in Neotropical rainforests, Golden Carpenter Ants are covered in a layer of long, dense golden (or sometimes silver) hair.

ATTACK AND DEFENSE

ANTS ARE NOTORIOUS TO GARDENERS and outdoors folk alike for their ability to bite or sting at an unexpected moment. They have an extensive arsenal of physical and chemical defenses at their disposal. Ants use hairs, spines, and teeth for attack and defense, yet their most lethal weapon is located at the pointy end of the body. The subfamily Formicinae have an acidopore, a conical structure surrounded by hairs that squirts formic acid at any would-be attackers. In contrast, the subfamily Dolichoderinae have a slit-like opening with no hairs or sting. Other major subfamilies possess a venom-delivering sting for subduing prey or defending themselves. An internal poison gland produces either formic acid (in the Formicinae) or venom.

Ants have dorsal spines, protrusions of the cuticle on the upper surface of the body. They usually extend from the propodeum, pronotum, or petiole. Spines range in length and curvature from small bumps to elaborate branched structures. Considering the impressive spinescence of ants, the function is not studied in many species. In contrast to other ornate structures, such as the horns of Stag Beetles, ant spines are not a product of sexual selection in males but are most strongly displayed in the female workers. Unlike close relatives such as bees and wasps, wingless ant workers cannot fly away. It is thought that ant spines make it harder for vertebrate predators to capture and eat ants as well as for other invertebrates to attack them. Spines have evolved

BELOW LEFT: This species of *Polyrhachis* has three separate pairs of defensive spines on their pronotum, propodeum, and petiole.

BELOW: *Acanthognathus ocellatus* is a Neotropical Trap-Jaw Ant that uses its rapidly closing mandibles to catch springtails and other small leaf-litter arthropods.

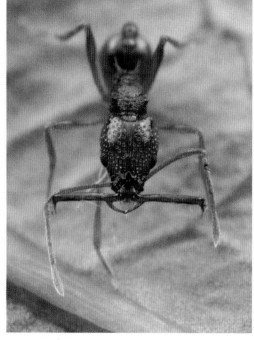

repeatedly in many different and unrelated species, being present in at least 79 of 346 genera, most commonly in the megadiverse subfamily Myrmicinae.

Jaws, or mandibles, are highly modified for feeding and in predatory species especially for hunting. As well as mandibles being used in direct attacks, they can be used to hold a prey item while a sting is deployed or to pin the prey in place while other workers dissect the unlucky individual. Trap-Jaw Ants have specialized mandibles that are held in an open position and have trigger hairs that, when tripped, cause the jaws to shut with extreme force. While these jaws are used mainly in hunting, they can also be co-opted as a defense mechanism to escape predators. Examples of Trap-Jaw Ants have evolved multiple times in different subfamilies, including in *Myrmoteras* within Formicinae, in the Myrmicinae subfamily for *Daceton* and *Strumigenys*, and in Ponerinae for *Anochetus* and *Odontomachus*.

Some species have different worker castes, with one specifically assigned a role in defense and usually referred to as soldier ants. These are often larger than other workers in the colony. Another physical defense strategy is phragmosis. Phragmotic species have truncated body structures that are used to block the entrance to their nests. This is most commonly seen in the head of ants from genera such as *Colobopsis*, *Cephalotes*, and *Pheidole*. *Cephalotes*, better known as Turtle Ants, have shield-like heads that can be used to plug the entrance to their nest without exposing the eyes or antennae. In *Cephalotes varians*, the head perfectly fits the nest entrance and the guard ant can allow other workers to enter and exit the nest while ensuring that any potential intruders are denied access.

BELOW: Major *Colobopsis etiolata* worker ants have an abruptly truncated phragmotic head. They use their head to block the entrance hole of nests in dead branches or oak galls.

BELOW RIGHT: Defensive structures include a sting (top left), an acidopore (top right), and a slit-like opening used to smear chemicals (bottom).

ANT DEFENSE

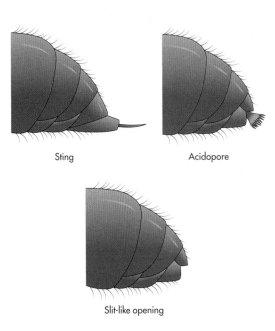

Sting

Acidopore

Slit-like opening

LOCOMOTION

A RELATIVELY SMALL SUBSET of all ants use flight to get around, with wings mainly present in males and queens. Sometimes reproductive ants are wingless or show a reduction in wings (with short and long wings present in different morphs of the same species), but generally they have two pairs of soft membranous wings. The requirement for wings is because reproductives move much greater distances away from their birth nest in order to mate and in the case of queens to found a new colony. Workers move on foot, either to and from a central nest or with a colony in nomadic species. They usually move over the ground or vegetation, often through confined spaces, none of which would be feasible with two pairs of membranous wings. This means that the morphology of ants differs wildly depending on the caste of the individual being considered.

MUSCLES

Queens have a morphology more typically seen of flying insects, with an enlarged thorax to carry the musculature required for wings. In most flying insects the first thoracic segment is small while the second and third are larger as each supports a pair of wings. The thorax arrangement for queens depends on their colony-founding strategy and therefore how they make use of their wings. Non-claustral species are those where the queen will actively hunt to feed the first generation of workers. Queens perform a high amount of foraging and their first thoracic segment is much closer in size to workers', with their wing and neck muscles more balanced in size. In contrast, claustral queens do not forage or go through a worker-like phase. They metabolize their own wing muscles to provide the energy needed for production of the first

THORACIC MUSCLE ARRANGEMENTS

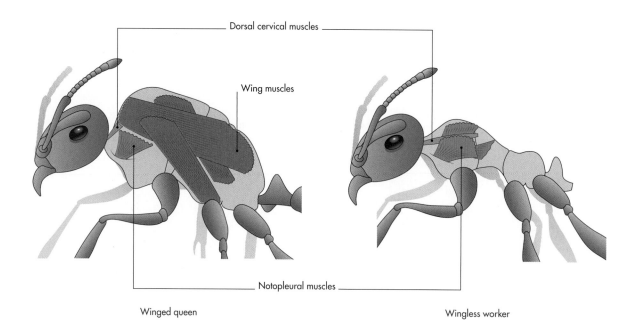

Winged queen

Wingless worker

generation of workers and therefore have a reduced neck segment while the wing muscles are enlarged. In contrast to the queens, worker ants show an enlarged first segment of the thorax and the muscles associated with it. This gives greater strength and mobility to the neck, which is in control of head movements.

LEGS

Ants have three pairs of legs that vary in size and shape to reflect the environment they occupy as well as their feeding habits. These legs are named according to where they attach to the body. They are pro-, meso-, and meta-, referring to the first, second, and third pairs of legs. The basal segment where the leg anchors to the body is the coxa. From there is found the trochanter, a relatively small segment, followed by the longer femur and tibia—equivalent to a human thigh and shin. The final section is the tarsus, which has five subsegments and terminates in a pair of claws—sometimes with a membranous lobe, the arolium, between the claws. The tibia sometimes possesses spurs that may be modified on the forelegs as a specialized device for cleaning the antennae.

OPPOSITE: The structure of thoracic muscles is very different for winged queens (left) who have highly developed muscles for flight, unlike wingless workers (right).

BELOW: Ant legs can be highly modified depending on how and where a species lives and forages, but they all follow the same broad plan for each leg of coxa, trochanter, femur, tibia, and tarsus.

LEG STRUCTURES

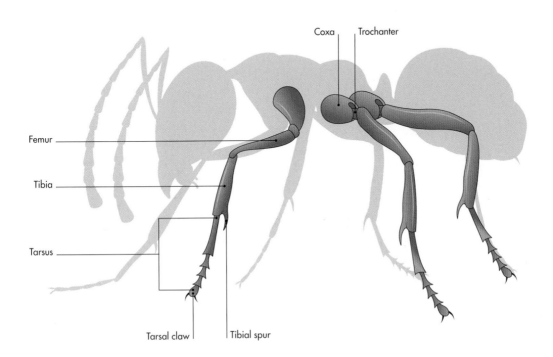

Coxa Trochanter

Femur

Tibia

Tarsus

Tarsal claw   Tibial spur

SENSORY STRUCTURES

EYES

Ants have two compound eyes composed of many facets known as ommatidia. Eyes have been lost completely or reduced in many subterranean species, contrasting with a number of predatory species that have extremely large eyes for hunting. The more ommatidia, the better the spatial resolution of the ant's vision. In ant species with large eyes, ommatidia numbers can be as high as 4,100 (in *Gigantiops*) and 3,200 (*Myrmecia*). Additionally, several species have ocelli on their forehead. These are light-sensitive eyespots that likely have a role in navigation. Ocelli are usually absent in workers and more commonly seen in queens and males. Ants are not primarily visual insects, and in ant brains the optic lobes are much smaller than are seen in close relatives such as wasps and bees. This may be because most ants do not fly and those that do spend only a small part of their life flying. Ants spend less time relying on visual sensory cues and are more heavily reliant on other senses such as

chemicals. They can perceive UV light and have color vision, although this is likely limited to only a few colors. Ants also process other visual information about motion, patterns, directions (position of the sun, polarization pattern of the skylight), and landmarks.

ANTENNAE

While ant reliance on visual cues varies across species, all ants rely heavily on chemical communication and use their antennae as their main sensory organs. The antennae are typically elbowed, consisting of 4 to 12 individual shorter segments called antennomeres. The base of the antenna is one long, single segment—the scape. This is followed by the funiculus, which is made up of multiple shorter segments. Segments in the funiculus may be of equal size or gradually increase in width. Occasionally a few of the end segments form a bulbous club. The scape and funiculus form an elbowed joint, a unique feature of the ants. The antennae nestle within a socket on the front of the head. Some species of ants have antennal scrobes—grooves on the sides of the head that the antennae can be retracted into.

Antennae are moved around by muscles inside the head as well as in the base of the antennae. These muscles are controlled by the dorsal lobe in the brain, which receives mechanical sensory information input from the antennae. Olfactory receptor neurons in the antennae are connected to the antennal lobe. Antennal lobes are large in ants relative to other insects because they rely more on smell than sight and because they use pheromones for communication. Antennal lobes can process ordinary smells as well as pheromones.

LEFT: Based on the number of ommatidia, *Gigantiops destructor* has the largest eyes of any ant, which it uses to locate prey while foraging in the forests of South America.

MOUTHPARTS

Ants have biting and chewing mouthparts, often with distinctively shaped and well-developed mandibles. Ant mouthparts have an upper lip (labrum) and lower lip (labium). They also have a pair of mandibles and maxillae. The maxillae and labium each have sensory palps that can feel and smell food as it is being eaten. Mandibles are typically triangular in shape, with a smooth outer edge and a toothed inner masticatory margin. However, mandibles have evolved into a vast array of shapes and sizes, from toothless to double-forked teeth on the masticatory margin, to overall shapes that are variously short or elongated, straight or curved.

Mandibles are used by ants for a variety of tasks, including feeding, attacking, and defending, as well as handling and manipulating objects. Mandibles are used for excavation and construction of nests. Carrying behavior in ants requires a specialized skeletomuscular modification of the head and neck muscles. Some ants are known to carry prey between 30 to 90 times their own weight and perform delicate controlled head movements while carrying these objects. As well as food items, ants will also carry liquids suspended as a drop between their mandibles. Worker ants will carry brood (eggs, larvae, and pupae) to move them around different parts of the nest or to a new nest location. This requires a sensitive touch using mandibles in a careful and deliberate way so as not to damage the soft-bodied early life stages of the colony. Finally, ants are even known to carry each other.

ABOVE LEFT: Located above the eyes, the antennal scrobes of *Mycetomoellerius tucumanus* are visible as deep channels on the top of the head.

ABOVE: The trap-jaw mandibles of *Myrmoteras iriodum* have 12 teeth and are usually held open at 280 degrees. These, and large compound eyes, make these ants efficient hunters of small prey.

INTERNAL ANATOMY

NERVES

In the ant nervous system, bundles of nerve cells form ganglia that are connected by nerve cords to create the central nervous system. There is essentially one long nerve cord running from the brain through to the abdomen with branching nerves along it. Ant brains are like most insect brains, containing different regions that relate to various, often sensory, functions. The optic lobes are the visual centers, comprising the lamina, medulla, and lobula, while the antennal lobe is the primary olfactory center. There are also protocerebral lobes, the central body, and the mushroom body (made up of the calyx and the mushroom body lobes). Fused to the back of the brain is the subesophageal ganglion. This bundle of nerves branches into the mouthparts and acts in sensory detection and muscle movement. These nerves also control the head and neck movements. Following on from the subesophageal ganglion is the first thoracic ganglion. This then forms a chain of ganglia that run through the body as thoracic, petiolar, and gaster ganglia, although the numbers of ganglia are not well known in many ant species. The mushroom body may be involved in cognitive functions such as learning and memory. The role of the central body in ants is unknown but may be related to organizing behavior, for example in polarization vision or leg control. On average, larger ants have larger brains, with males having smaller brains than female queens and workers.

CIRCULATION AND RESPIRATION

While an ant's respiration occurs in metabolically active tissue, the process of gas exchange (receiving oxygen and removing carbon dioxide) occurs through spiracles—tiny holes in the exoskeleton. Spiracles are connected to trachea, and these are connected to even finer branching tracheoles that perform gas exchange with cells throughout the body. Gas exchange can occur by diffusion of the gases through the tracheal system, where a continuous movement of oxygen and carbon dioxide occurs. Some ant species show discontinuous gas exchange, where there is a cyclical pattern created through the opening and closing of spiracles at different times, meaning that oxygen is taken in during activity and carbon dioxide is released during rest periods. The respiration system of ants delivers oxygen directly to tissues, reducing the requirement for a circulatory system to perform gas exchange. Ants have an open circulatory system with a single long tube running the length of the body that is equivalent to the heart. A pulsing movement moves hemolymph around the ant's body. Hemolymph is the ant equivalent of blood; it moves nutrients, hormones, and waste around the body while also circulating hemocytes—cells responsible for insect immunity.

DIGESTION

Ants follow the same basic digestive system plan as most insects in that they possess a fore-, mid-, and hindgut. The foregut is the most complex, containing the oral cavity, followed by the pharynx, esophagus, crop, and proventriculus. The esophagus is a long tube that moves food through the insect body to the crop, a ball-shaped sac that acts as a food storage area and is located within the gaster. In ants the crop, often referred to as the "social stomach," is used by foraging worker ants to store liquid foods such as nectar or insect honeydew. In a process known as trophallaxis, this food is then regurgitated and shared out among other members of the colony. The proventriculus is a muscular valve that facilitates the process of trophallaxis. Any food allowed to pass into the midgut is digested by the ant, but food held in the crop due to the constriction of the proventriculus is part of the food supply for the colony's social stomach. The proventriculus also acts as a separation point to prevent digestive enzymes from the midgut flowing into the crop. Digestion occurs in the midgut, where absorption of nutrients takes place. The hindgut function is devoted to the process of reabsorption of water and salts.

INTERNAL BODY SYSTEMS

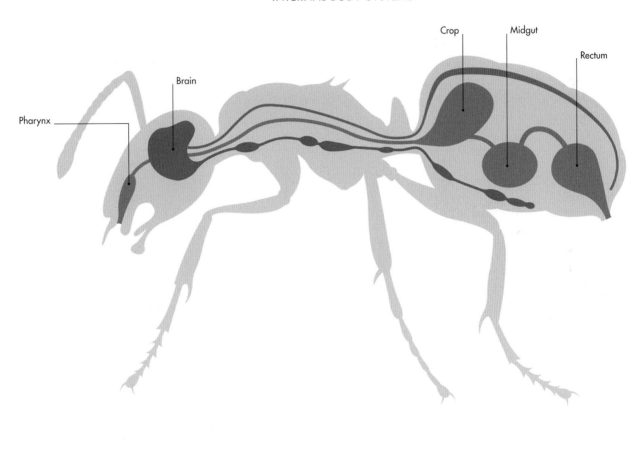

Pharynx

Brain

Crop

Midgut

Rectum

ABOVE: The internal organs of ants include the brain and nervous system, the circulatory system, and the digestive system.

KEY

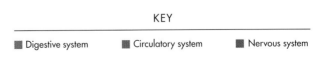

■ Digestive system　　■ Circulatory system　　■ Nervous system

REPRODUCTION

RELATIVELY LITTLE IS KNOWN about ant copulation. It occurs with a male on top of, and facing the same direction as, a female, although exceptions are frequently observed. The male grasps a female by the legs and then probes with his genitalia before eventual penetration. The external genitalia are complex, with a large number of components serving different functions such as anchoring and clasping the male ant to the female. While internal reproductive organs are formed of soft tissue, the external genitalia are sclerotized. As well as being highly complex, the male genitalia exhibit a wide variety of different shapes across ant species.

Broadly, the external male genitalia comprise a ring of muscle at the base, known as the cupula, followed by three layers of paired valves: the outer parameres, the middle volsellae, and the inner penisvalvae. The outer parameres are used for grasping, while an inner serrated blade-like structure of the penisvalvae is thought to act as an anchor during copulation. Internally, male ants have testes as well as accessory testes and accessory glands. In the notorious Fire Ant, *Solenopsis invicta*, males have four testes that appear as four white lobes and are at a maximum size during a late pupal stage of development. They then turn amber and degenerate as the male reaches maturity. Hundreds of sperm are arranged with their heads oriented in one direction within sperm packets, of which there are many inside a follicle of the testes. The accessory testes comprise ejaculatory secretions and a sperm reservoir where sperm are kept in mature males. There is then an accessory gland that produces seminal fluid and this is attached to the external genitalia.

RIGHT: Mating of these *Brachymyrmex patagonicus* ants shows the relative size difference that occurs in some species between a smaller male and a much larger queen.

We know even less about female reproductive anatomy than we do for males. Females have two ovaries that are formed of several ovarioles. These have the appearance of strings of beads that are developing oocytes (eggs). The ovaries are connected to the uterus by the oviducts. As queen ants usually only mate at the beginning of their adult life, they need a way to store sperm. After mating with a male, a queen will store sperm inside a specialized structure called a spermatheca. This means sperm can be used as and when required to fertilize oocytes.

BELOW LEFT: A model of a female ant reproductive system based on images of *Eciton burchellii,* an Army Ant queen.

BELOW RIGHT: Ants follow an approximation of the same general model of the internal reproductive system for a male insect that can be seen here, although anatomical details vary between species.

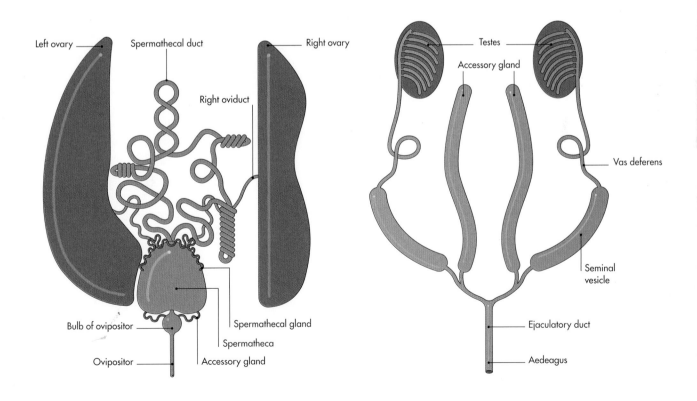

FEMALE REPRODUCTIVE SYSTEM

Left ovary — Spermathecal duct — Right ovary

Right oviduct

Bulb of ovipositor — Spermathecal gland

Spermatheca

Ovipositor — Accessory gland

MALE REPRODUCTIVE SYSTEM

Testes

Accessory gland

Vas deferens

Seminal vesicle

Ejaculatory duct

Aedeagus

ODONTOMACHUS
Trap-Jaw Ants

SUBFAMILY:	Ponerinae
DIVERSITY:	73 species
DISTRIBUTION:	Tropical and subtropical regions with highest diversity in the Neotropics and Asia
HABITAT:	Usually forest, sometimes scrub or estuarine
NEST:	Soil or rotting wood, abandoned termite nests, or trees
DIET:	Generalist predators, some omnivores

Odontomachus are omnivores and generalist predators, feeding on invertebrates (especially termites), honeydew, nectar, fruits, and seeds. Their most distinctive feature is their long, straight mandibles, often held open at 180 degrees. They belong to a wider group of Trap-Jaw Ants who all have rapidly closing mandibles released by trigger hairs.

FASTEST MANDIBLES
An ant's mandible is attached by a hinge with two muscles, an opener and a closer. The closer is the largest muscle ant workers have. Trap-Jaw Ants have modified this arrangement to include a latch, spring, and trigger mechanism. The latch holds the mandibles open at 180 degrees and the spring stores potential energy. When the trigger muscle is activated, the mandibles shut instantaneously. In *O. bauri* the mandibles close at a top speed of 210 ft (64 m) per second or 143 mi (230 km) per hour, making it one of the fastest animal movements ever recorded.

The trap-jaw mechanism is used in hunting and defense. Ants locate prey by sight until within striking distance and use their trap-jaws to complete the attack. Prey may be hit repeatedly with the mandibles to break it up. "Bouncer" ants at nest entrances will snap their jaws to push away intruders using a strike force 300 times greater than their own body weight. They are also known to escape from predators using the power generated by mandible closure to propel themselves backward to safety.

HUNTING PROWESS
As well as their formidably powerful jaws, *Odontomachus* ants use their large eyes and well developed sting for hunting prey.

GIGANTIOPS

Gigantiops destructor is immediately recognizable from its enormous eyes, but spotting one in the first place may be difficult. These shy ants can identify humans from several feet away and will run and jump into a hiding spot. Colonies have several hundred individuals, yet workers are solitary foragers, collecting extrafloral nectar from plants and hunting various live arthropod prey (especially termites). They nest in cavities of fallen *Cecropia* trees, in the soil, under logs and stones, or in root cavities.

FINDING YOUR WAY IN THE FOREST

Only one to three *Gigantiops* workers in a colony of a hundred will forage for prey items. Workers stack food in their mandibles, hunting up to eight small termites in a single trip. Prey are tracked visually from behind and pounced on, even flying prey. Workers in a colony will fight over food, sometimes snatching a captured prey item from the jaws of their nestmate, a behavior called cleptobiosis.

Gigantiops return to the same feeding spot for up to five weeks using an established route between the nest and food source. In the complex rainforest environment, they cannot employ the navigation methods commonly used by other species such as chemical trails, skyline panoramas, or canopy orientation. Instead, they navigate using known landmarks, relying especially on the first landmark near their nest to determine their direction, as well as final landmarks to confirm the location of their feeding site.

SUBFAMILY:	Formicinae
DIVERSITY:	Monotypic (one species)
DISTRIBUTION:	Countries of northern South America
HABITAT:	Forest and savannah, usually rainforest
NEST:	Ground-nesting. Cavity-nesting.
DIET:	Omnivores

LONE FORAGER
Although they are solitary foragers, *Gigantiops destructor* ants nest along rainforest edges in colonies with many hundreds of workers.

POLYRHACHIS
Spiny Ants

SUBFAMILY:	Formicinae
DIVERSITY:	Fourth-largest ant genus with over 700 species. Diversity hotspot is in Southeast Asia.
DISTRIBUTION:	Found throughout tropical and subtropical Africa, Asia, Australia, and the Pacific islands
HABITAT:	Forest, woodland, savannah
NEST:	Ground, leaf litter, and arboreal, including in carton nests or leaf structures woven together with larval silk
DIET:	Generally omnivorous, including scavenging for insects, tending aphid mutualists, and sucking excretions from plant wounds

As one of the most diverse and conspicuous genera in the tropics, these ants exhibit stunning variation in morphological traits and ecological behavior. True to their name, most species sport varying numbers of spines, formed from pointy extensions of the cuticle on the dorsal surface of the body. As likely defenses against vertebrate predation, spine size and shape range from tiny needles to giant fishhook-shaped protrusions. The surface of many species are covered with tiny gold, silver, or white pubescence (hairs) that may serve as warnings to predators of the danger of their spines.

NATURAL INNOVATORS

While best known for their spines, Spiny Ants have evolved a number of interesting responses to nature's challenges. Some arboreal species have abandoned more direct defenses altogether, losing their spines and instead relying on an unexpected behavioral defense: dropping off a leaf and plummeting down to the forest floor. These and most other arboreal species repurpose larval silk to bind leaves and other material together to form nest structures in the trees, with a few species even stealing spider silk for their constructions. When threatened with flooding, the mangrove forest-dwelling species *P. sokolova* can swim across the water with a dog paddle swimming stroke. As the tide rises and the subterranean nest is submerged, workers relocate the queen and brood to special air pocket chambers, allowing the colony to survive until the tide recedes.

FINE GOLDEN HAIRS

The unmistakable gold pubescence and hooked spines belong to *Polyrhachis ypsilon*, an ant species found in Brunei, Indonesia, Thailand, and Malaysia.

CAREBARA

Carebara are ground-nesting ants found in many habitats of tropical or subtropical regions. They are a diverse genus that display distinct size patterns of workers relating to their roles inside the colony. *Carebara* ants show extreme size variation, with workers ranging in total length from $^3/_{64}$ in (1 mm) in the Neotropical *C. minuta* up to $^5/_8$ in (16 mm) in the Oriental *C. diversus*. Size divergence is exhibited for different worker castes—a large major may weigh up to 500 times as much as a small minor.

MAJOR OR MINOR?

Division of tasks is related to size and age. Majors account for 10 percent of the colony's workers. They aid with dissecting and transporting larger prey as well as colony defense. A special subcaste of major workers are phragmotic—their heads are shaped into shields used to block nest entrances against attackers. Minor workers carry larvae while young but gain other responsibilities as they age.

Whether workers vary in size depends on the individual species. Some species are all a similar size (monomorphic), while others have a distinct division into two size groups (dimorphic). Sometimes the size variation follows a gradual increase or is seen in more than two groupings (polymorphic). It is common to see multiple sizes in the major workers, which exhibit differences in head size, number of ocelli, and eye size. Some species like the Malagasy *C. jajoby* and *C. nosindambo* have up to four distinct-sized major workers.

SUBFAMILY:	Myrmicinae
DIVERSITY:	223 species
DISTRIBUTION:	Global distribution, concentrated primarily in the tropics and subtropics
HABITAT:	Multiple habitat types, often within forests
NEST:	Ground-nesting in rotten logs, leaf litter, under stones
DIET:	Specialized predators, including on mites, springtails, and arthropod eggs

FROM ONE EXTREME TO THE OTHER
Minor *Carebara* workers are dwarfed by a single individual major worker who is many times their size.

MELISSOTARSUS

SUBFAMILY:	Myrmicinae
DIVERSITY:	4 living species, 1 fossil species
DISTRIBUTION:	Mainland sub-Saharan Africa, Madagascar, and Saudi Arabia
HABITAT:	Forests, and infest orchards. Inhabit around 20 tree species.
NEST:	Arboreal. Tunnel nests under bark in live wood.
DIET:	Probably omnivore

The tiny and rotund *Melissotarsus* ants live a secretive life contained entirely within their arboreal nest galleries under tree bark, where up to 1.5 million ants occupy a single tree. From head to tarsus they are perfectly adapted to a life of tunneling. They have zinc-reinforced chewing mandibles powered by well-muscled heads, meaning they can chew through live wood. Excavation tunnels are repaired and reinforced using silk secreted from the heads of workers—the only example of silk production known in adult ants. The front pair of legs is used to maneuver the silk into position. Oddly, the middle pair of legs faces upward, in the opposite direction of the front and back pairs, allowing ants to brace against tunnel walls. In fact, ants removed from their nests will often stagger and topple over.

BUG FARMING

The diet of *Melissotarsus* is a mystery. They never forage outside their nest and live intimately with armored scale insects (Diaspididae) of 13 different species. Diaspids are a legless bug that inject enzymes into plants and then feed on the predigested plant material. *Melissotarsus* may feed directly on live diaspids, farming them like cattle, but it seems more likely they eat wax secretions produced by diaspids as well as dead or dying diaspids and the discarded skin of diaspid larvae. Workers may also be able to digest plant cytoplasm during their excavation of live-wood tunnels.

GEOGRAPHICAL DISTRIBUTION

This species, *Melissotarsus weissi*, is found in mainland Africa along with *M. beccarii* and *M. emeryi*. The fourth species in the genus, *Melissotarsus insularis*, lives on Madagascar and nearby islands.

HARPEGNATHOS
Jumping Ants

Jumping Ants are ferocious hunters of fast-moving or jumping prey including crickets, cockroaches, cicadas, flies, and spiders. They are large, up to $^{25}/_{32}$ in (2 cm) long, and possess huge forward-facing eyes, long legs, and scythe-shaped jaws with more than 50 sharp teeth. They are solitary crepuscular hunters that rely on visual hunting strategies and their excellent vision, thanks to having the largest number of ommatidia of any ant species. Their forceps-like mandibles have fast muscle fibers that ensure rapid closure on captured prey, which can then be subdued with a powerful sting that causes permanent paralysis.

JUMP AROUND

As their common name suggests, *Harpegnathos* are best known for their jumping abilities. While Trap-Jaw Ants use their large mandibles to generate an explosive force for jumping, in *Harpegnathos* the jump is powered by their long legs. Jumping can form part of normal locomotion, but when under threat ants will perform an escape jump of up to 8 in (21 cm), sometimes repeatedly, until they reach safety. Shorter jumps are used in hunting fast-moving prey and sometimes to capture flying insects in mid-air. A fourth jumping behavior is "group jumping": an ant will jump around in a seemingly random fashion for no reason, and after a few minutes other worker ants will join in. Nobody knows why they perform this collective behavior, but it could be to flush out prey or prevent parasitoid attacks.

SUBFAMILY:	Ponerinae
DIVERSITY:	9 species, 4 subspecies
DISTRIBUTION:	India to Sri Lanka and Southeast Asia
HABITAT:	Forests and plantations
NEST:	Hypogaeic. Complex nest architecture in some species.
DIET:	Solitary predator. Hunts in leaf litter for fast-moving arthropod prey.

INSIDE THE NEST
Harpegnathos saltator keep their flood-prone nest chambers dry by pasting the inner walls with debris including old cocoon, insect, and plant parts.

TATUIDRIS
Armadillo Ants

SUBFAMILY:	Agroecomyrmecinae
DIVERSITY:	Monotypic (one species)
DISTRIBUTION:	Neotropics
HABITAT:	Forest
NEST:	Ground-nesting
DIET:	Unknown, presumed to be predatory

The rounded appearance of *Tatuidris tatusia* explains why its name means Armadillo Ant. It is not just the single representative of a species within its genus *Tatuidris*, but also one of only two species in its entire subfamily, the Agroecomyrmecinae. It is found in a range of forest types. Based on the small number of individuals collected at any one time, it is considered rare, yet it is locally abundant in mid-elevation premontane forest.

DISCOVERING DIETS

Usually collected by leaf litter sifting and vegetation sweeping, no living *Tatuidris* ants were found until 2011. Seven individuals were discovered in a soil core taken in Ecuador and kept for 19 days to study their feeding behavior. In captivity, the Armadillo Ants would not accept any food, including live and dead prey, honey, or sugar water. This could be due to the stress of being in captivity or because they only feed after actively hunting their prey.

Given the lack of feeding behavior observed, scientists turned to other forms of evidence to understand their diet. Stable isotope analysis revealed that *Tatuidris* are predators at the top of the arthropod food chain. On the underside of their mandibles, *Tatuidris* have many long, stiff hairs—a mandibular brush. They also have stiff hairs on their front legs, in addition to a large sting and a rounded, smooth body. From this evidence, scientists believe Armadillo Ants are specialist predators of large, slippery arthropods.

PATTERNS OF PILOSITY

While *Tatuidris tatusia* is only a single species, it has four different morphs that all have distinct patterns of pilosity. Being relatively rare, most available images are of nonliving specimens.

2 | EVOLUTION AND DIVERSITY

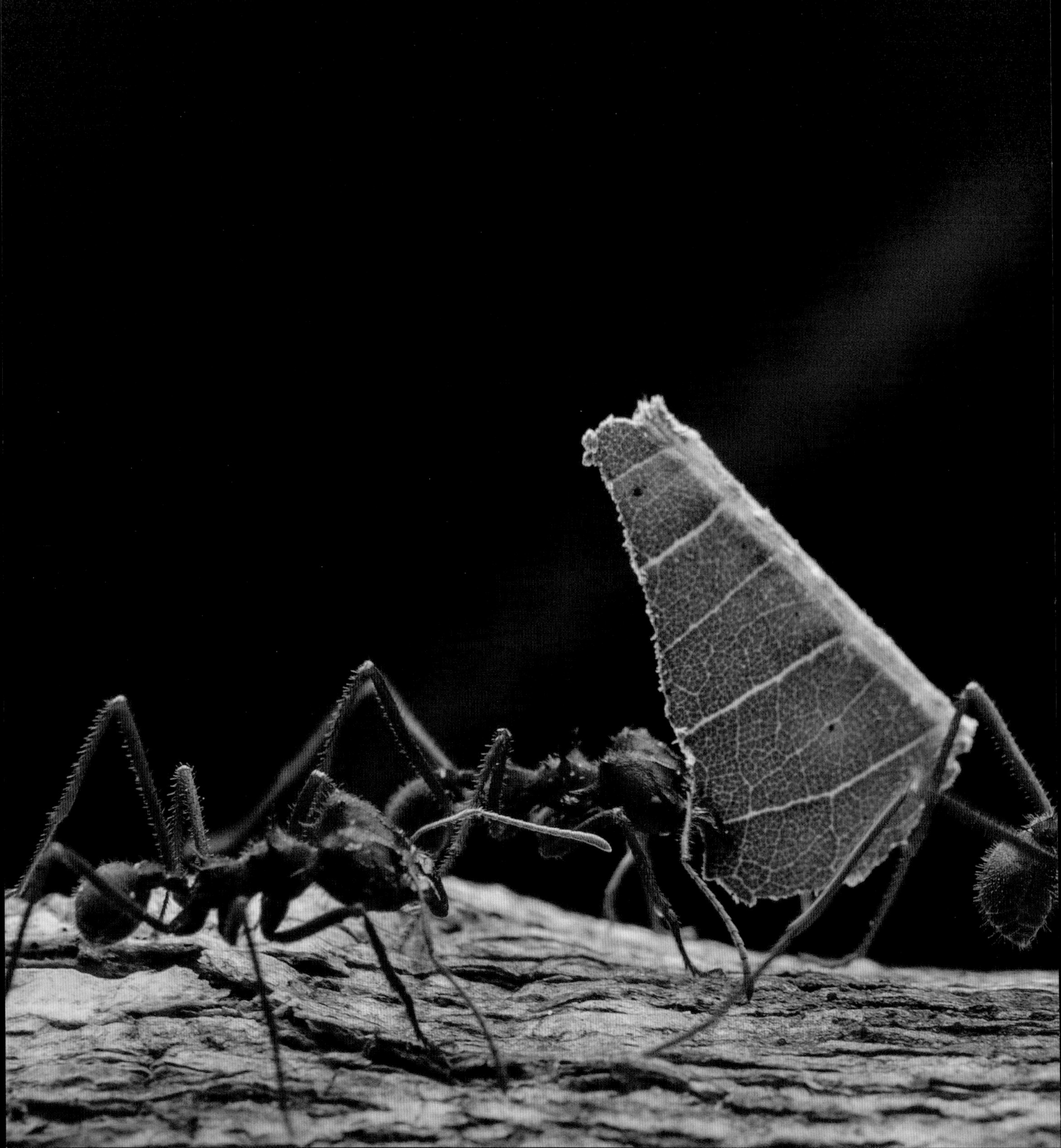

THE ANT TREE OF LIFE

ANTS, AN EVOLUTIONARILY SUCCESSFUL group in their own right, are situated within the highly diverse taxonomic order Hymenoptera: wasps, bees, sawflies, and (last but not least!) ants. With over 150,000 extant species described, Hymenoptera is among Earth's largest insect orders and is only significantly dwarfed by Coleoptera (beetles). For decades, entomologists hotly contested the exact placement of Formicidae within Hymenoptera, with some researchers hypothesizing that ants are most closely related to wasp groups that do not include bees. However, recent studies in the field of phylogenomics utilizing DNA sequences from across the genome of various species have firmly established that ants are evolutionarily nested within the stinging wasp subclade and are most closely related to the Apoidea superfamily, which includes bees and "sphecoid" wasps. In the same manner that birds are in fact evolutionarily derived dinosaurs, ants are evolutionarily derived wasps.

While Formicidae, with about 14,000 known species, contains comparable diversity to Apoidea, with around 20,000 species, ants are distinct from their sister group and the rest of Hymenoptera in a few key ways. First, as discussed in Chapter 1, ants are morphologically unique, with a distinct petiole of one or two segments, elbowed antennae, and a metapleural gland (subsequently lost in some species but considered a "basal" trait of the ants). Second, all ants are eusocial (Chapter 3), whereas in bees and wasps, sociality ranges from solitary to eusocial, with intermediate subsocial, communal, quasisocial, and semisocial species. And third, although some bee and wasp species are wingless, nearly all ant species contain wingless workers and either winged or wingless queens and males. The only exception to this rule is in evolutionarily derived socially parasitic ant species that have evolved the loss of a worker caste in favor of parasite queens that rely on care provided by workers from the parasitized colony. These differences between ants and the rest of Hymenoptera may have set ants along an independent evolutionary trajectory resulting in unique outcomes for their ecology, morphology, and global diversification.

As within Hymenoptera, Formicidae is subdivided into smaller taxonomic groups. These 16 extant subfamilies and 6 extinct subfamilies vary widely in number of described species, from as low as a single species in Martialinae to as high as over 7,000 species in Myrmicinae. It is often quite difficult, especially without genetic data, to definitively determine the relationships between and within clades that diverged so many millions of years ago, and thus subfamily designations and hypotheses about their relationships to each other have shifted considerably over recent decades. The former subfamily Heteroponerinae, for example, was designated a subfamily in 2003, but genomic data collected nearly two decades later revealed that the group is in fact a tribe of a different valid subfamily, Ectatomminae. Similarly, the placement of Martialinae was impossible prior to 2008, as the very existence of the single species and genus in this subfamily was only reported in 2008!

Such recent changes among primarily species-poor groups notwithstanding, the subfamily designations for the vast majority of species are increasingly stable, supported by a growing number of studies incorporating genomic-scale data. The "Big Five" major subfamilies, encompassing 93 percent of all ant diversity, are Myrmicinae, Formicinae, Ponerinae, Dorylinae, and Dolichoderinae. The remaining minor subfamilies are Agroecomyrmecinae, Amblyoponinae, Aneuretinae, Apomyrminae, Ectatomminae, Leptanillinae, Martialinae, Myrmeciinae, Paraponerinae, Proceratiinae, and Pseudomyrmecinae. Most fossil species have been placed in one of these extant subfamilies, but the six described extinct subfamilies, encompassing 5 percent of all known extinct diversity, are Armaniinae, Brownimeciinae, Formiciinae, Haidomyrmecinae, Sphecomyrminae, and Zigrasimeciinae.

PHYLOGENY OF LIVING ANTS

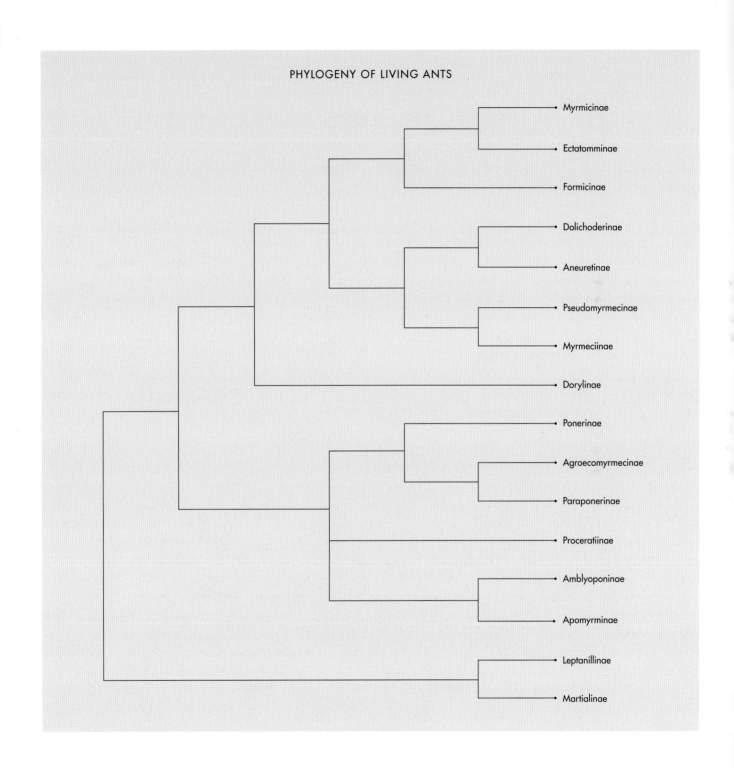

- Myrmicinae
- Ectatomminae
- Formicinae
- Dolichoderinae
- Aneuretinae
- Pseudomyrmecinae
- Myrmeciinae
- Dorylinae
- Ponerinae
- Agroecomyrmecinae
- Paraponerinae
- Proceratiinae
- Amblyoponinae
- Apomyrminae
- Leptanillinae
- Martialinae

THE BIG FIVE

MYRMICINAE

With 7,075 described species, about 50 percent of known ant diversity, the myrmicines are the undisputed powerhouse of Formicidae. As befits such hyperdiversity, species in this subfamily exhibit about as much morphological and ecological variation as can be found across all ants. Along with Agroecomyrmecinae, Pseudomyrmecinae, and Dorylinae (another Big Five subfamily), species in this subfamily possess a subdivision of the petiolar abdominal segment into a petiole and postpetiole, which potentially allows for more flexible movement. The diet of myrmicine species ranges from carnivorous to herbivorous and fungivorous, including live and dead insects, plant sap and other exudes, seeds, and various other food sources. Similarly, different species can be found in nearly every microhabitat, from twigs in the forest canopy down to large subterranean caverns. Some of the most iconic ant genera are found in this subfamily: Fire Ants, Leafcutter Ants, Turtle Ants, Pavement Ants, Harvester Ants, Big-Headed Ants, and Thief Ants are all members of Myrmicinae. The subfamilies most closely related to the myrmicines are Ectatomminae and Formicinae.

BELOW: A Maricopa Harvester Ant (*Pogonomyrmex maricopa*) worker battles a trio of *Aphaenogaster* workers in the southwestern United States.

OPPOSITE TOP: *Echinopla* is a unique genus in Formicinae. Numerous erect hairs cover the ant's body, giving it an appearance like a porcupine.

FORMICINAE

This subfamily may not boast the diversity of its cousin Myrmicinae, but with a respectable 3,244 described species it is nonetheless formidable. Some of the most common formicines are also some of the most conspicuous of all ants, including Carpenter Ants, Weaver Ants, and Spiny Ants. The largest two genera in the subfamily (*Camponotus* and *Polyrhachis*, together comprising 55 percent of Formicinae) predominantly occupy trees, and their dominance of this niche could partially explain the evolutionary and ecological success of this clade. A defining trait of these ants is the acidopore—a circular opening at the end of the gaster that can spray formic acid in lieu of a stinger (whence comes the name "Formicinae"). This subfamily is most closely related to Myrmicinae and Ectatomminae.

RIGHT: Heavily armored *Polyrhachis armata* Spiny Ants conspicuously forage in long trails from the ground up into the high canopies of Southeast Asian rainforests.

LEFT: Perched atop a small piece of wood, this *Hypoponera distinguenda* worker from Minas Gerais, Brazil is only about ⅛ in (4 mm) long.

PONERINAE

With 1,267 described species, this subfamily is one of two in the Big Five that are predominantly predacious. An exception to this general rule, perhaps surprisingly, is one of the largest ants in the world: the Giant Amazonian Ant *Dinoponera gigantea* is omnivorous. Several genera are specialized predators on prey such as isopods, termites, millipedes, and other ants. As a result of this predacious behavior, species in this subfamily typically utilize a functional sting to subdue prey. In contrast with Myrmicinae and Formicinae, most ponerine species forage in the subterranean or leaf litter strata. A distinguishing morphological trait in this subfamily is a constriction of the gaster that gives it a somewhat pinched appearance. While the iconic members of Ponerinae are very large, some species, including those in the diverse genus *Hypoponera*, are quite small and inconspicuous. The subfamilies Agroecomyrmecinae, Paraponerinae, and Proceratiinae are most closely related to the ponerines.

DORYLINAE

A subfamily of 749 species, the dorylines are exclusively predacious as nomadic Army Ant foragers. The colonies of some species are quite small, with only a few dozen workers, while colonies of *Dorylus* Driver Ants can contain millions of workers. Foraging trails of some larger doryline colonies are so massive and voracious that human observers can predict the arrival of the ants by the insects and other animals that flee ahead of the advancing colony, which vacuums up most of the smaller dead and living insects and even smaller

mammals and lizards in its path. Some species have well-developed eyes, but most have either very small eyes or are even entirely blind, relying exclusively on chemical cues via their antennae to navigate underground tunnels or paths in the leaf litter. Due to the subterranean foraging behavior of many species, much remains to be discovered about the biology of numerous species in Dorylinae. However, more is known about the males of some species in this subfamily than for most ants in other subfamilies, due to their unusually large and tubular morphology that led to their common name, Sausage Flies. Dorylinae are most closely related to a large clade of seven subfamilies including Myrmicinae, Formicinae, and Dolichoderinae.

DOLICHODERINAE

The smallest of the Big Five, this subfamily contains 714 current species. As in Formicinae, workers in this subfamily lack a sting, but instead can produce chemicals from an anal gland out through a slit in the gaster. Due to these chemicals, many species exude characteristically strong odors when disturbed or crushed—the Odorous House Ant *Tapinoma sessile* is said to smell like blue cheese or rotten coconut. Species tend to be scavengers, although some are generalist predators, and typically have a particular fondness for sugary food sources like plant exudes or the sugars excreted by herbivorous insect mutualists like aphids and caterpillars. Dolichoderines appear to have less often evolved distinct morphological traits compared to most other subfamilies, sometimes rendering species-level taxonomic categorization

BELOW: The sugary excretions of aphids are a common food source for dolichoderine ants such as the *Technomyrmex* foragers seen here.

RIGHT: *Dorylus* Driver Ants, also called Safari Ants or Siafu (derived from Swahili), are arguably the most important arthropod predators in the African tropics.

quite challenging, but workers in the subfamily can often be identified by relatively erratic movements along foraging trails. The subfamily most closely related to Dolichoderinae is Aneuretinae, which together are sister to Myrmeciinae and Pseudomyrmecinae.

RISE TO DOMINANCE

ANTS MAY BE NEARLY ubiquitous in most ecosystems across Earth today, but of course this was not always the case. Based on a combination of fossil evidence and phylogenetic inferences, the common ancestor of ants was likely a wasp-like insect species that nested in the soil or in leaf litter and diverged from Apoidea around 150 million years ago (MYA) or even earlier. Despite this early origin, current evidence suggests a long lag period before the true rise of the ants as an ecologically dominant and evolutionarily diverse group of Hymenopteran insects. There are no ant specimens in the fossil record prior to 100 MYA. Furthermore, the fossil record from 100 to 78 MYA includes only two species that can be clearly placed in subfamilies that remain today. Genetic evidence, which was crucial in inferring an older age of ant origins, corroborates this species-poor early period of ant evolution, with phylogenetic studies inferring origins for the major subfamilies of around 60–80 MYA. So, why did it take so long for ants to really flourish?

One popular theory arises from a couple observations. First, most of the largest groups of ants, such as Myrmicinae, Formicinae, and Dolichoderinae, have diverse associations with angiosperms (flowering plants) either directly or indirectly through insect herbivore mutualists like aphids,

BELOW: The larvae of some species of *Leptanilla* have a special duct organ that allows queens to feed from their hemolymph.

caterpillars, and scale insects. Second, an increase in diversification in ants appears to coincide with the rapid diversification of angiosperms, which now make up nearly all plant species. Therefore, in a sort of coevolutionary dance, the rise of the angiosperms may have driven the rise of the ants. As further supporting evidence, Martialinae and Leptanillinae, which are small, ground-nesting ants believed to have retained many of the ancestral traits of early ants, diverged very early from the rest of ants over 100 MYA and together consist of 69 species—a mere 0.5 percent of extant diversity. This clade may have maintained such low diversity due to remaining bound to the ground, without the evolution of associations with angiosperms that could have driven diversification in other subfamilies. Ultimately, angiosperm-driven ant evolution is a compelling story with some supporting evidence, but it may not be possible to determine with certainty the cause (or causes!) that led to an explosion of ant diversity.

DEEP TIME CAPSULES

FOSSILIZED ANTS ARE HELPFUL for understanding the origins and subsequent evolution of ants, and the search for fossils has led to some fascinating discoveries of traits that no longer exist among extant ants. Most of the ant fossil record consists of hardened amber fossils derived from tree sap that trapped or otherwise encased a living ant and then hardened, preserving the specimen for millions of years. There are also numerous ant specimens fossilized in stone, which are called impression fossils. Generally, amber fossils are most valuable to scientists as they typically preserve the entire morphology of the ant, whereas impression fossils preserve a two-dimensional outline that may be difficult to confidently identify to species, genus, or occasionally even subfamily. The ages of ant fossils are estimated, with some margin of error, based on the dating of amber or rock deposits where the fossils are found. Beyond helping to guide evolutionary inferences based on DNA data alone, which has been shown to be biased in the absence of fossil data, fossil finds have demonstrated that some ants as early as 100 MYA had already evolved some highly specialized traits. A prime example is *Haidomyrmex*, a genus of so-called Hell Ants, which sported bizarre, curved trap-jaw mandibles that snapped in a vertical direction, in contrast to all modern Trap-Jaw Ants with mandibles that move horizontally.

Fossils can also directly validate hypotheses about ecological interactions and behaviors, preserving interactions between species in real time. Ant paleontologists have discovered ancient amber fossils that encapsulated two wingless female ants from the same species together, as well as a fossil of an adult wingless ant with a wingless pupa. These represent snapshots of likely eusocial behavior, namely nonreproductive workers foraging together and a worker caring for brood. Several ant species discovered in Baltic amber deposits (dated to 34–48 MYA) are found with aphids, supporting the theory that angiosperm-facilitated mutualistic interactions between ants and plant sap–sucking insects is not only a recent phenomenon. The predacious diet of the Hell Ants and the vertical trap-jaw function of their mandibles were recently definitively proven with the discovery of a fossil worker ant grasping a cockroach-like prey between its jaws and the horn-like structure that protrudes from its head. A Leafcutter Ant trapped in Dominican Republic amber shows evidence of mutualistic bacteria on its exoskeleton, revealing that such a relationship present in modern Leafcutter Ants is at least 15–20 million years old.

TECHNOLOGICAL ADVANCES

Amber deposits are limited geographically and only represent a subset of time periods between the origin of ants to the present, so existing ant fossils are a precious but highly incomplete record of ant evolution and ecological interactions through time. However, despite a far smaller number of ant paleontologists compared to vertebrate paleontologists, there are about the same number of described fossil ant species as there are fossil dinosaur species. Furthermore, recent technological advances have led to the use of X-ray

LEFT: Groups of ants in amber can provide data about historical social behavior and ecological interactions.

microtomography, or micro-CT scanning, to non-destructively produce high-quality 3D images of fossil ants encased in amber. Such images produced by micro-CT scanning increase the amount of accessible data that ant paleontologists can retrieve from amber fossils. With continuing and increased research on amber and impression ant fossils, and the implementation of novel techniques, many new and informative discoveries await.

ABOVE: A well-preserved myrmicine ant from a prehistoric Baltic amber deposit dating to 34–48 million years ago.

INNOVATION AND TRADE-OFFS

THE ABILITY OF ANTS TO evolve a wide range of morphological (structural) traits is both remarkable and fundamental to ants' evolutionary, ecological, and geographical expansion and persistence. Much of this trait variation is detailed in the ant profiles throughout this book. Body length in ants ranges from $\frac{1}{32}$ in (0.8 mm) (*Carebara bruni*) to $1\frac{37}{64}$ in (4 cm) (*Dinoponera gigantea*), a 50-fold difference. Ant colonies can contain fewer than ten workers or as many as a million. Numerous species have evolved a dimorphic worker caste, meaning morphologically distinct workers that serve different functions (foraging for food versus defending the colony, for example), while most species are monomorphic without discernibly discrete differences. Some species have several small, thornlike cuticular spines or even massive fishhook spines that can exceed the length of the mesosoma, while others have no spines at all. Many species have a rough exoskeleton covered in hairs (pilosity), while others are smooth and shiny. Mandibular shape varies from small and weak pincer-like jaws to long and robust trap-jaws that upon striking a surface can propel workers into the air up to 20 times their body length. Some ant workers that forage in the trees have massive eyes that are nearly as long as their heads, yet others have entirely lost their eyes and forage underground or in the leaf litter. When provoked by a vertebrate attacker, the colonies of certain species will mount a robust response with dozens, hundreds, or even thousands of swarming workers deploying painful chemicals through a stinger. By contrast, workers of some species with earthy coloration evade threats by pressing their bodies against the surrounding surface to hide via camouflage, while in others, foraging workers take the drastic measure of dropping from twigs and gliding downward toward the ground to escape harm.

Such variation within a single family of Hymenoptera is striking enough on its own. But it is additionally notable that across the ant tree of life, or "phylogeny," there are numerous

independent evolutionary gains (and losses) of many important traits like those listed above, including large body size, worker polymorphism, spines, specialized mandibles, and large colony size. Evolutionary biologists call this "convergent evolution." Repeated convergent evolution of these traits as well as the innovative evolution of unique traits indicate that Formicidae is generally quite adaptable. As local environments changed over millions of years, different

LEFT: The queens of many *Carebara* species are much larger than the smallest workers, which can be as tiny as ³⁄₆₄ in (1 mm) (*Carebara minuta*).

ABOVE: *Polyrhachis bihamata* workers sport enormous defensive spines and can release formic acid, but do not have a sting or soldier subcaste.

traits could continue evolving to increase adaptability to new conditions, including the loss of traits that no longer increased survival within an ant population. This adaptability is not without its limits, with one recent study finding that there is an evolutionary trade-off in defensive traits in ants—species with a functional sting were less likely to evolve a suite of other defensive traits than those without a sting. Similar trade-offs also exist within an ecological community of ant species—ant species with certain traits more successfully exploit certain nesting and diet resources, while ant species with different traits more effectively utilize different resources. To put it simply: No one species can express all possible traits that would be maximally adapted to all possible conditions, able to consume all food resources from fungus to small lizards or to live in every microhabitat from a tropical forest canopy to desert sand. These trait trade-offs,

on both shorter ecological and longer evolutionary timescales, likely allow for many species to persist and new species to evolve, precluding the dominance of only a small handful of species that would drive all others to extinction.

It is intriguing that despite the ample evolvability of ants as a group, all ants are eusocial with no true solitary species. In contrast, there is evidence in other groups with eusocial species, like bees and aphids, that eusociality is sometimes lost. The genetic basis of eusocial behavior in ants could be so multifaceted and complex that the subsequent evolutionary loss of the trait is virtually impossible. At least so far, such a strong evolutionary constraint does not appear to be acting as a so-called "evolutionary dead end," where an evolved trait

ABOVE LEFT: *Odontomachus simillimus* mandibles are highly specialized to produce rapid movement as an adaptation to catch prey such as springtails.

ABOVE: A *Paraponera clavata* stinger delivers venom that produces intense pain for up to 24 hours. It is considered the most painful of all insect stings.

may be beneficial in the short term but limits speciation or increases risk of extinction in the long term. In fact, the preserved eusociality of the ants could be a major contributor to their global success as a group. However, some future environment could exert strong enough of a natural selection pressure to render eusocial behavior disadvantageous and result in some population of one ant species losing eusociality, giving rise to the first solitary ant species.

A COSMOPOLITAN GROUP

ANTS ARE PRESENT ON EVERY continent except Antarctica—don't let the name fool you! There are species recorded in every country in the world except for a handful of geographically isolated island nations such as Iceland and Maldives. Like many animal and plant groups, species diversity is concentrated in the tropics, with ant diversity decreasing as latitude increases from the equator to the poles. There are many possible reasons for why this pattern exists—ants, which generally prefer moisture and have numerous associations with trees and insect herbivores, may flourish in humid tropical and subtropical environments that contain a high diversity of tree species. A couple general theories about this observed latitudinal gradient of diversity are the "museum" hypothesis and the "cradle" hypothesis. The museum hypothesis proposes that due to various factors at higher latitudes, including greater seasonal variation and ice ages that caused large glacier formations to form, species existing closer to the equator can persist with lower extinction rates compared to those found in the sometimes uninhabitable and cold higher-latitude regions. The cradle hypothesis, on the other hand, posits that tropical habitats generate more new species compared to temperate habitats even if the extinction rate for existing species is the same. One recent study in ants found evidence for both hypotheses, finding that ant species went extinct at a lower rate in the tropics (museum) and that the speciation rate was higher in the tropics than in the temperate zone (cradle).

Outside of such broad patterns, ant biogeography is defined by significant variation with distributions differing widely in geographical location and breadth depending on the

BELOW LEFT: *Camponotus* Carpenter Ant pupae are protected by cocoons spun from larval silk. Depending on the species, pupae are either cocooned or "naked."

BELOW: *Strumigenys louisianae* carrying a larva. Ant larvae cannot excrete waste, visible here as dark spots inside the larvae, until they reach the pupal stage.

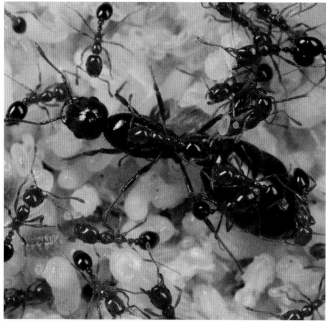

subfamily, genus, and species. A handful of larger genera—including *Pheidole, Camponotus, Strumigenys, Crematogaster, Solenopsis,* and *Hypoponera*—are truly global with at least a few species on every continent. But there are several cases where a genus has undergone significant speciation and geographic expansion but is nevertheless confined to a subset of continents. The Spiny Ant genus *Polyrhachis,* for example, is widespread throughout tropical and subtropical Africa, Asia, the Pacific islands, and Australia, but contains zero species in Europe, North America, or South America. The Wood Ant genus *Formica* is nearly ubiquitous across the entire Northern Hemisphere yet is entirely absent from the Southern Hemisphere. The genus *Tetramorium* is found from South Africa all the way to eastern Russia, contains a few species native to North America and Central America, and includes the invasive Pavement Ant *Tetramorium immigrans,* yet South America is devoid of even one native *Tetramorium* species. These variable patterns likely arise from a complex set of environmental, ecological, and historical factors.

ENVIRONMENTAL INFLUENCES

Natural selection pressures in different environments have produced a variety of ecological behaviors in ants, which are discussed in further detail in Chapter 5. For example, seed predation among Harvester Ant species like *Pogonomyrmex barbatus* is especially prevalent in more open, drier, and arid regions like the deserts of the southwestern United States, perhaps owing to the higher availability of seeds and the difficulty of procuring alternative food resources that are common in wetter tropical and temperate habitats. The complex relationship between Leafcutter Ants and fungal mutualists requires enough moisture to support the fungi and enough accessible leaf material for the ants to feed to the

ABOVE: The cuticle of the Philippine ant *Polyrhachis cyaniventris* is an iridescent blue, a rare coloration among all animal groups including ants.

ABOVE RIGHT: Once ant–fungus mutualism evolved, Leafcutter Ants like *Atta cephalotes* gained access to a consistent food source not available to other ants.

RIGHT: *Pheidole hartmeyeri* drags a ryegrass seed in Western Australia. Seed consumption may contribute to this species' high tolerance for environmental stress.

fungi, and it is thus not too surprising that Leafcutter Ants are primarily found in tropical and subtropical habitats in the Americas. Unlike some insects, no ant species can live underwater or spend significant time in water, but in some regions that are particularly prone to tidal flooding, like in the Amazon Basin or tropical mangrove forests, some species have evolved workers that can swim short distances or even link bodies with nestmates to form living rafts. In general, there is a close relationship between the geographical and climatic features of a region and which ant species and behaviors are found in that region.

ISLAND LIVING

ALTHOUGH SOME ISLAND NATIONS hold the distinction of being the only countries without any native ants, many islands host especially diverse ant communities. Due to a steep rise in elevation on volcanic islands, such as those in Indonesia and Fiji, the variations in temperature and humidity that determine ant distribution patterns on a global scale can all exist together on a single island. Volcanic island systems are also regularly generating new habitats through the emergence of new islands, and so the age of different islands in an archipelago can vary by tens of millions of years. This variation could in turn lead to a higher number of ant species, as well as especially unique species specialized to different microhabitats. Yet the two most important factors in island ant diversity may be the surrounding ocean water and island size variation. As ants cannot inhabit water, the isolation between islands strongly limits the movement of ants between them, which in turn promotes genetic isolation that can ultimately lead to the evolution of distinct species. When compared to smaller islands, larger islands typically contain more exploitable resources and habitable land as well as a more diverse biological community overall. Correspondingly, islands that are more remote, as well as

LEFT: The invasive Yellow Crazy Ant *Anoplolepis gracilipes* can form polygynous supercolonies with as many as 1,000 queens.

OPPOSITE: The island of Madagascar boasts a comparably high diversity of six known species of *Stigmatomma* Dracula Ant.

RIGHT: Fungus-Growing Ants such as *Mycetarotes* are distributed throughout continental South and Central America yet are rarely found on islands.

those that are smaller, tend to have fewer ant species than those that are larger and less isolated from nearby islands or closer to potential continental sources of colonization.

Ants were the inspiration for a theory that incorporates these principles, called the "taxon cycle," which proposes to explain the observation that more unique, specialized ant species were more common in the island interior, which is away from the coastline and typically at higher elevations. According to taxon cycle predictions, the initial phase of expansion across islands is driven by generalist species that are both adept dispersers and typically found along coastlines or in

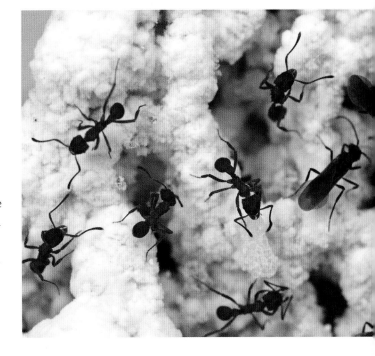

disturbed habitats. Over time, the different populations of such "supertramp" species diverge into different species, including some that become well adapted—or specialized—to the more complex island interior habitats. Along with such specialization, some ant species progressively lose the generalized traits of the ancestral populations. There is some evidence that the hypothesized taxon cycle does explain the distribution of ant species across the Melanesian islands, but the general applicability of the theory has not been well established. One complicating factor is anthropogenic (human) dispersal of ant species and disturbance of lowland island habitats. As more specialized species tend to be more sensitive to disturbance, it is plausible that human housing development and other environmental disruptions, which disproportionately impact flatter coastal regions, drive the observed higher prevalence of specialized ant species in island interior habitats. If so, then the patterns addressed by the taxon cycle, which operates over an evolutionary timescale, could instead arise from more recent phenomena. The recent rapid spread of the Yellow Crazy Ant, *Anoplolepis gracilipes,* an invasive ant species, across the Pacific islands is one such example of anthropogenic inter-island dispersal. The role of humans in the spread of ant species, and in particular invasive ant species, is covered further in Chapter 6.

Like in true islands, continental mountain systems also promote diverse ant communities through island-like mechanisms. The environmental gradient along large mountain slopes is even more extreme than on islands, with the harsh conditions above 6,500 ft (2,000 m) resulting in very few ant species present at such high elevations. Furthermore, given mountain geometry, the total available area for colonization is smaller at higher elevations compared to lower elevations. Thus, parallel to smaller islands supporting fewer species than larger islands on average, it is already expected that high-elevation mountain regions would contain fewer ant species than lowland regions even if all other environmental factors were similar. Given the existing differences between high-elevation and low-elevation habitats along mountain slopes, ant species that are specialized to high-elevation habitats and are not present in lowland habitats are, ecologically, on an island. Across a mountain range, populations significantly upslope on one mountain cannot easily disperse to upslope habitats of other mountains nearby, isolated not by ocean water but rather an expanse of uninhabitable terrestrial habitat.

LEFT: A *Pheidole* worker feeding from a *Jatropha podagrica* extrafloral nectary (EFN). Plants use EFNs to recruit ant defense against herbivores.

OPPOSITE: Massive *Formica rufa* mounds are a common sight in European lowland forests. Some evidence suggests these Wood Ants shift their behavior in advance of earthquakes.

LEFT: *Oecophylla smaragdina*
Weaver Ants are highly successful
in both continental and island
habitats and are resilient against
human disturbance.

NOTHOMYRMECIA
Dinosaur Ants

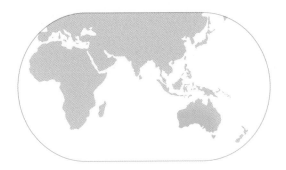

SUBFAMILY:	Myrmeciinae
DIVERSITY:	Monotypic (one species)
DISTRIBUTION:	Australia
HABITAT:	Woodland
NEST:	Ground-nesting
DIET:	Omnivores

Nothomyrmecia macrops is a medium-sized yellow ant with elongated triangular mandibles and large eyes. This exceptionally timid ant is a solitary nocturnal forager of insect prey and honeydew. They form small colonies of 50 to 100 workers and live in old-growth mallee and Eucalyptus woodland. Nests are typically small holes in the ground under shallow leaf litter. *N. macrops* possesses many physical features of a primitive ant. It is similar in appearance to ants that lived 60 MYA, hence its name, the Dinosaur Ant.

HUNTING FOR DINOSAURS

In 1931 a collection of general insects was made in Western Australia and passed to amateur entomologist Amy E. Crocker. She sent two specimens of an unusual-looking ant to John S. Clark. He described the new species in 1934, and its primitive appearance sparked huge interest in the myrmecological community. Expeditions to find the ant took place at the original collection site in 1951 and continued unsuccessfully for another 20 years. In 1977 a party of entomologists were camped in South Australia. Lo and behold, who should they stumble across but *Nothomyrmecia*, over 40 years later and 800 mi (1,300 km) away from the original location. The Dinosaur Ant is perhaps the only ant species in the world with its own tourism industry. In Poochera (the rediscovery site) there is a large *N. macrops* statue, and pictures of the ant are stenciled on the streets.

REGAL FEATURES
Queens of *Nothomyrmecia macrops* possess ocelli (eyespots) and a ventral stridulatory organ. They can be brachypterous, meaning they have short wings that cannot be used for flight.

CREMATOGASTER

Acrobat Ants

Crematogaster ants are found in forests and savannahs around the globe. They can be easily recognized by the postpetiole (the second segment of their waist) that attaches on top of a heart-shaped gaster. The gaster is typically flexed high in the air in a defensive posture observed if these highly territorial ants are disturbed. This is the root of the common name Acrobat Ants, in reference to how they balance precariously waving their sting, ready to strike their enemies.

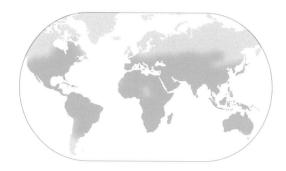

THE PATH TO GLOBAL DOMINANCE

Acrobat Ants first arose in Southeast Asia in the mid-Eocene between 40 and 45 MYA. Over the next 15 million years they stayed in Southeast Asia evolving and diversifying into the three major lineages existing today. Their path to worldwide colonization began with expansion into Africa, followed by a spread into the Americas, Europe, and Australia through complex dispersal patterns that took place multiple times by different lineages of *Crematogaster*. This suggests a predisposition as excellent colonizers, perhaps because of a high survival probability due to large-bodied queens and large colony sizes. Another theory on their success relates to transoceanic dispersal ability. In tropical regions, *Crematogaster* nest arboreally within dead branches, underneath loose bark, or in specially constructed nests made of carton—a material made up of plant debris. This tree-nesting habit may have allowed them to float across oceans cocooned safely inside plant material.

SUBFAMILY:	Myrmicinae
DIVERSITY:	Over 500 species. Diversity is concentrated in the tropics.
DISTRIBUTION:	Found globally with species on all major continents
HABITAT:	Forest, woodland, savannah
NEST:	Tropical species nest arboreally with some found in soil and leaf litter. Temperate species mainly nest on the ground.
DIET:	Generalist omnivores. Many feed on homopteran honeydew.

ABDOMINAL FLEXIBILITY

The attachment of the postpetiole high on the fourth abdominal segment gives *Crematogaster* ants the flexibility to maneuver their gaster over their torso.

PHEIDOLE
Big-Headed Ants

SUBFAMILY:	Myrmicinae
DIVERSITY:	1,171 valid species
DISTRIBUTION:	Global, most diverse in the Neotropics
HABITAT:	Virtually all temperate and tropical habitats
NEST:	Ground-nesting and arboreal
DIET:	Omnivore

Pheidole is the most diverse ant genera, containing 8 percent of all known ant species. They have successfully expanded around the globe into tropical and temperate forests, grasslands, and deserts. Despite being found everywhere except the coldest environments on Earth, the number of *Pheidole* ant species found in a given place correlates closely with the climate, especially with higher temperatures and levels of rainfall. In the Neotropics (or New World) there is a higher richness of species compared to the same climate in Old World regions. For example, the ant community of a Neotropical wet forest is made up of 18 percent *Pheidole* species, compared with 11 percent in Old World wet forests.

NEOTROPICAL ORIGINS

Modern lineages of *Pheidole* ants arose around 37 MYA in the Neotropics. They then went on to colonize all regions of the globe, undergoing geographically localized evolutionary radiations. This means that they moved into Africa, Asia, Australasia, and New Guinea at individual points in time. From there they underwent diversification to evolve into the many hundreds of species that exist in these regions today, with virtually no exchange of species between continents once established. The ability to colonize a new habitat type was a result of an evolutionary transition within a geographic area, rather than because a species from a similar habitat elsewhere dispersed to that locality.

GENUS DIVERSITY

With more than 1,000 currently described species and a worldwide distribution, the taxonomy of *Pheidole* is in need of revision before the final number of species can be confirmed.

STRUMIGENYS

Strumigenys is the third-most species-rich ant genus, reaching high diversity in tropical and subtropical rainforests. These small ants (less than ⁵/₃₂ in or 4 mm long) nest in soil and leaf litter with a few arboreal nesting species. Some have trap-jaws for rapid prey capture and are specialist predators of springtails.

DESCRIBING NEW SPECIES

When scientists discovered a new and unusual *Strumigenys* species in Ecuador, they knew it needed a special name. Most *Strumigenys* have highly patterned exoskeletons with flattened sesame-seed-like hairs covering their body. The newly discovered ant had fine hairs and no surface sculpture, giving it a smooth, shiny appearance. It was described as *S. ayersthey* to honor the artist Jeremy Ayers, one of Andy Warhol's "Superstars." Traditionally, new species named after individuals are given the appropriate Latin suffix to reflect gender. This is -ae for female, -i for male, and -orum for a group. The use of the suffix -they in *S. ayersthey* is for people who do not identify with conventional binary gender assignments and who have previously been unrepresented by traditional taxonomic naming practices.

In another modern twist on traditional taxonomy, six new species of *Strumigenys* ants from the Fiji islands were described in 2019 using augmented reality. Anyone can download a mobile phone app that turns tiny tropical ants into giant superimposed 3D images available to view in their own home.

SUBFAMILY:	Myrmicinae
DIVERSITY:	858 species
DISTRIBUTION:	Found globally
HABITAT:	Forest, shrubland, plantation
NEST:	Ground-nesting. Rarely arboreal.
DIET:	Predators

ELBOWED ANTENNAE
This *Strumigenys* worker ant perfectly displays the typical elbowed antennae that are a defining characteristic of all ants.

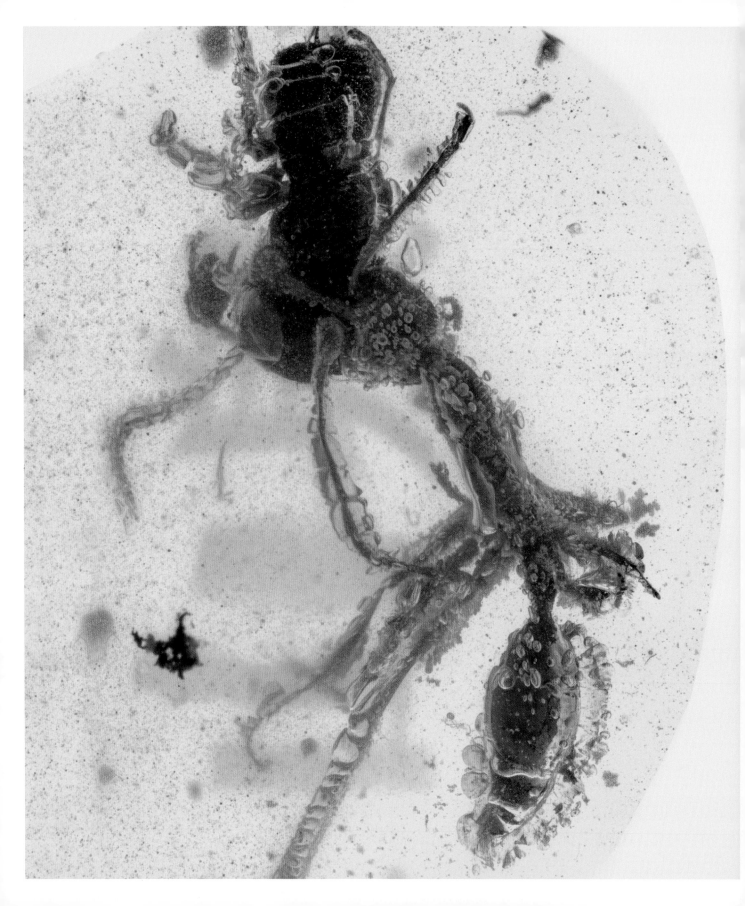

HAIDOMYRMECINAE
Hell Ants

SUBFAMILY:	Haidomyrmecinae
DIVERSITY:	Extinct: 10 genera, 16 species
DISTRIBUTION:	Amber from Canada, France, and Myanmar
HABITAT:	Unknown
NEST:	Unknown
DIET:	Predators

There are 730 fossil ant species known from 67 deposits. Many are placed in extant (living) subfamilies, but some are not recognizable as belonging to modern groups. The subfamily Haidomyrmecinae are an entirely extinct group known as the Hell Ants that are unlike anything alive today. All specimens of Hell Ants are known from around 100–79 MYA, in the mid-Cretaceous period. They are found primarily in Burmese amber with a small number of specimens from French and Canadian amber.

A PREDATOR FROM HELL

Hell Ants have upwardly pointing scythe-like mandibles and a horn protruding from their forehead. Modern ant mandibles open in a lateral plane, moving from side to side. The bizarre Hell Ant mandibles move up and down using a trap-jaw mechanism to capture prey. The horn of a Hell Ant is an extension of the clypeus, the (usually) flat front plate of the head. Hell Ants had two methods of prey capture. *Haidomyrmex* and other similar Hell Ants had extremely sharp mandibles thought to be used to impale their prey. Ants like *Ceratomyrmex* had smooth, elongated horns and would have pinned prey between their mandibles and horn. They could then use their sting on the immobilized prey. This hunting behavior is captured in a Burmese amber fossil of *Ceratomyrmex ellenbergeri*. The ant can be seen pinning the neck of a cockroach between its mandibles and horn.

ANCIENT PREDATOR
Preserved in amber, the Hell Ant *Ceratomyrmex ellenbergeri* (right) can be seen grasping its prey (top left). The horn is visible, protruding from the ant's forehead and wrapped around the prey.

MARTIALIS
Martian Ants

This is a one-of-a-kind ant. Workers are small, pale, blind, and virtually unknown to science. It is represented by one species for the entire genus, and a whole subfamily was created especially for it. The name *Martialis* refers to the bizarre characteristics of the ant that led scientists to joke that it could be from Mars.

DISCOVERING MARTIAN ANTS

In 2008 *Martialis heureka* was described based on a single worker discovered walking on leaf litter through primary lowland rainforest. Two workers were collected five years earlier, but tragically on the way from the field site to the Museu de Zoologia in São Paulo the lid of the collection vial opened, causing the ants to dry out. Despite efforts to remove these precious specimens from the vial intact, eventually it was broken open and the fragmented ant pieces collected and studied. No further workers have ever been discovered, but in contrast 25 males have been collected, as these can be intercepted at flight traps.

Martian Ants could be a relict, the only surviving species representing ants that arose early in the history of ant diversification—ants that hung on to ancient physical characteristics living in the relative stability of tropical forest soils. These ants are the sister group to all known living ant species, suggesting that when early ants were evolving they were cryptic ground-nesting foragers that later expanded into the other environments where they thrive today.

SUBFAMILY:	Martialinae
DIVERSITY:	1 species
DISTRIBUTION:	Manaus region of Brazil
HABITAT:	Rainforest
NEST:	Presumably ground-nesting
DIET:	Unknown but thought to be predatory based on mandibles

RARE SPECIMEN

This male *Martialis heureka* ant was collected in Brazil at a Malaise trap—a method used to intercept flying insects. Owing to the rarity of this species, most available images are of nonliving specimens.

DISCOTHYREA

SUBFAMILY:	Proceratiinae
DIVERSITY:	49 species
DISTRIBUTION:	Global distribution, concentrated in the tropics and subtropics
HABITAT:	Predominantly forest and woodland, sometimes grassland
NEST:	Ground-nesting. Leaf litter, humus, and concealed microhabitats.
DIET:	Unknown for most species but likely predators. When known, diet is arachnid eggs and juveniles.

These bizarre-looking ants have an enlarged abdominal segment that creates a curved C-shaped body. They are considered cryptic due to their tiny size and inconspicuous occupation of leaf litter. Some species are specialized predators of spider eggs, while others eat live spiderlings. In a colony-founding strategy termed claustral lestobiosis, ants establish nests in the egg cases of Tube Web Spiders.

CYBERTAXONOMY

A study of African *Discothyrea* ants in 2019 described 15 brand-new species. Uncovering so many new species in a small group is surprising but shows the large number of species waiting to be described by taxonomists, especially for insects dwelling in soil or leaf litter in tropical regions. Scientists used the cutting-edge cybertaxonomy technique of X-ray microtomography scanning to examine the tiny ants clearly. In this technique, cross sections of an individual ant are created from X-rays to produce a virtual and interactive 3D model at very high resolution with computer-based reconstructions. The process does not destroy, damage, or require dissection of ants, so it can be used on rarely found specimens.

WAKANDA FOREVER

One of the most memorably named new species is *Discothyrea wakanda*, which lives only in the Rwenzori Mountains in the Democratic Republic of Congo. In the Marvel universe of the Black Panther comics this is the location of the fictional nation of Wakanda—a peaceful, prosperous country that was never colonized, where ancient traditions coexist alongside modern technology.

BROOD MANEUVER

This worker of *Discothyrea mixta* can be seen handling brood members of the colony within its nest in Kibale Forest, Uganda.

LIFE CYCLE

THE LIFE HISTORY STRATEGIES of ants vary widely in different subfamilies, but all follow a basic life cycle of egg, to larva, to pupa, and then adult. In general, each colony begins with a queen (the foundress), a male (or sometimes multiple males), and a mating event. These unfertilized female queens and males leave the nest when they reach maturity and perform a nuptial flight. The synchronization of many individual winged ants emerging from multiple colonies means this is often a visibly notable event and is known in some countries as flying ant day.

THE QUEEN

The queen is a reproductive female with the ability to lay eggs. Most queens have wings. While many do not survive the nuptial flight due to predation by birds and other predators, those that do survive can be long-lived. The queens of the Black Garden Ant can live nearly 30 years! In contrast, males

are usually short-lived and die soon after mating. Thus, males in ant societies have essentially no social role beyond serving as a sperm package. A queen may copulate with one or more males during the nuptial flight, but afterward she does not mate again throughout her lifetime. Queen ants store sperm in a specialized internal pouch in their abdomen—the spermatheca—for use when required.

FOUNDING A COLONY

After mating, a queen will select a nest site and shed her wings. This is the founding stage in the life cycle of the colony. Within the nest site, a queen begins to lay eggs. These eggs then go through a complete metamorphosis, developing through multiple larval instars into pupae, and finally into adult ants. While there is much variation and few details known about most species, this process takes about a month or two. The first workers, known as nanitics or minims, are

OPPOSITE: The typical ant life cycle. Whether a fertilized egg develops into a worker or a queen is determined by a combination of genetic and environmental factors.

LEFT: Workers, queens, and males are reproductively and morphologically distinct. Workers and queens usually share more morphological traits with each other than with males.

smaller in size than successive workers and feed on eggs laid specifically for food by the queen, who in many species also internally digests her wing muscles to convert the energy into food for this first generation of workers. The queen remains in the nest with these nanitics and cares for them until they are adults and can leave the nest to forage. The food these workers bring back to the nest is then used to feed the queen and any other offspring. As the colony grows in number of workers, the queen's focus shifts to reproduction and workers take over all colony tasks including foraging, tending of eggs and larvae, and colony defense. Colony size increases as more generations of workers are successfully reared. This is the ergonomic or exponential stage of the colony life cycle.

Finally, the colony enters the reproductive stage. Although the adult ants in a colony predominantly consist of female workers, there are also alates: winged reproductive adults that can be unfertilized female queens or males. When these individuals reach maturity, they emerge from the nest and the life cycle begins anew.

ANT LIFE CYCLE

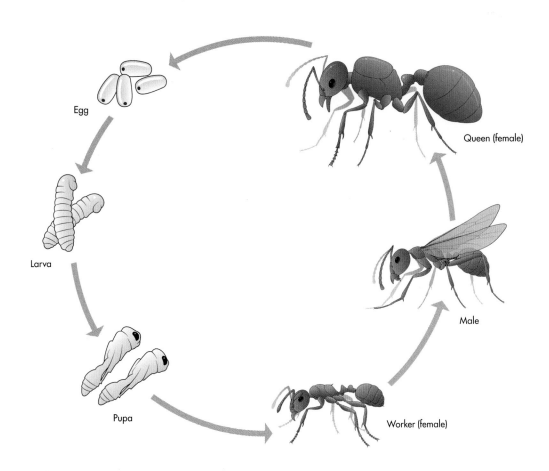

Egg

Larva

Pupa

Queen (female)

Male

Worker (female)

ABOVE: Two *Tapinoma sessile* queens together with visible wing scars. The Odorous House Ant forms polygynous colonies with more than one queen.

OPPOSITE: *Acromyrmex versicolor* Leafcutter Ant males take flight, waiting for unfertilized queens to join them in the air.

ABOVE: A *Lasius niger* Black Garden Ant queen with antennae extended, perhaps probing for environmental cues guiding a nuptial flight.

RIGHT: *Oecophylla* queens have a bulky mesosoma containing flight muscles that are internally digested to help feed the first generation of workers.

LOVE IS IN THE AIR

AS THE MAJOR MATING EVENT for most ant species, it is of the utmost importance to each species to synchronize the timing of the nuptial flight across different colonies of the same species to ensure that newly emerged males and unfertilized queens can meet. Emerged queens and males typically die within hours after leaving their origin nest if they fail to find a mate. Some species can release up to thousands of queens in under an hour, which is quite a substantial energetic investment. As a result of the necessity of nuptial flight synchronization with a high cost of failure, ants have evolved several behavioral and chemical traits to ensure successful mating events. Often a strong environmental cue will trigger male and unfertilized queen emergence in each colony. Relatively heavy rain is one such cue, because at that time conditions are favorable for forming new nests, particularly in otherwise dry habitats. Another mechanism is the release of pheromones by emerged males, which can be strong enough for humans to smell and most certainly strong enough to trigger the emergence of unfertilized queens from their nests. To avoid accidental mating between closely related species that live in adjacent habitats, some species have been observed conducting mating

events nearly exclusively in designated areas within the specific habitat type where each species nests, thereby spatially segregating the reproductives from each species.

The queens of some species, such as Leafcutter Ants, can mate with multiple males during nuptial flights. This results in a polyandrous colony with workers that have lower average relatedness than usual, as sister workers can share the same mother but have different fathers. The "patriline" (male lineage) of workers can be investigated and compared through population genetics methods, but without such techniques it can be difficult or impossible to firmly establish if a colony's

queen was mated by a single male or multiple males. Queens mating with multiple males could be a mechanism that increases genetic variation in a population, especially in species with a high risk of inbreeding, which might increase adaptability and survival in the long run. However, research into the nature and extent of polyandry in ants is at a very early stage, in part due to the previously unavailable genetic techniques necessary to investigate the subject, so much remains to be learned about the causes and consequences of the phenomenon.

ALTERNATIVE STRATEGIES

At the other end of the spectrum from polyandry are species whose queens do not participate in nuptial flights because they mate with no males at all. Instead, these queens can produce females, and not just males, with unfertilized eggs. The mechanisms allowing for this kind of process, called parthenogenesis, differ between species. In some species that parthenogenetically reproduce the female worker caste, the resulting workers are genetic clones of the queen. There are also a few species that vary in their deployment of parthenogenesis even within a single colony. The European ant *Cataglyphis cursor*, for example, produces queens through parthenogenesis but workers through sexual reproduction (that is, with sperm received during a nuptial flight). Perhaps the most bizarre reproductive strategy of all is found in the Little Fire Ant *Wasmannia auropunctata*. In this species, queens are produced through parthenogenesis, so they have no father. Males are produced through fertilized eggs, which

LEFT: Queen ants tend to be much larger than males, which have very short lives entirely dedicated to the mating event.

BELOW: Some ant queens mate with multiple males before founding a colony. This behavior may be depicted here, as the queen's wings are already removed.

RIGHT: In *Wasmannia auropunctata* colonies, new queens are produced through parthenogenesis, a form of asexual (clonal) reproduction.

is unusual in ants, but only fertilized eggs where the female genetic material is removed via a genetic mechanism within the zygote. Thus, males have no genetic mother and only a father. The sterile workers are produced by fertilized eggs that do not have the maternal genetic material removed in the zygote. The highly unusual result of this system is that this single species contains entirely genetically distinct lineages of reproductive males and reproductive females.

COLONY FOUNDATION— VARIATIONS ON A THEME

COLONY FOUNDATION IS A CRITICAL and delicate stage of an ant colony's life cycle. During this stage, queens are highly exposed to risks such as predation and weather conditions without the protection of workers whose traits will, after a colony is established, serve as her so-called "extended phenotype" (traits expressed in one organism for the exclusive benefit of a separate organism). Assuming she survives, a queen will search for a nesting site that she deems suitable, a determination that varies between species depending on which microhabitat the species is well adapted to. Many species that nest in leaf-litter habitat prefer nesting in "punky" wood (decaying trunks from fallen trees) due to the ideal soil moisture and potentially pre-existing structure of such substrate. Ants that nest under or between leaves in trees, like some *Polyrhachis* Spiny Ants or *Dolichoderus*

species, may search around for the right kind of leaves that are of the sufficient size and strength and malleable enough to be shaped into or support a nest structure. In twig-nesting species such as *Cephalotes* Turtle Ants, queens identify twigs that have pre-existing holes formed by wood-nesting beetles and, in the most specialized species, choose holes that perfectly match the circular heads that queens and soldiers use to protect nest openings.

Although solo colony foundation of a single nest is the most common behavior in ants, there are many variations on this theme. In some species, unrelated queens work together to establish a colony, a behavior called pleometrosis. Typically, after a colony is formed through pleometrosis, only one dominant queen is allowed to survive, and the others are killed or excluded from the colony. The Honeypot Ant *Myrmecocystus mimicus* follows this pattern. Alternatively, the multiple queens can together form a polygynous colony (a colony with more than one queen), as occurs in *Camponotus herculeanus* Carpenter Ants or *Iridomyrmex purpureus* Meat Ants. Polygynous colonies can also be formed in species that allow subsequently inseminated queens to join the established colony, or when separate colonies merge to form a single colony, although this is rare.

Forming polygynous colonies could have several advantages as well as disadvantages over standard single-queen, or monogynous, colonies. Collective foundation of a colony can be more efficient and succeed at a higher rate than solo foundation. When the queen dies in monogynous colonies, then the entire colony will slowly die out, as new workers are no longer produced to replace old workers after they die. By

LEFT: Weaver ant queens can cooperatively establish a colony, including jointly protecting their first cluster of eggs on a leaf.

LEFT: *Aphaenogaster fulva*, Winnow Ants, are often epigeic (aboveground) nesters. Here, they have established their colony in a fallen and decaying tree trunk.

BELOW: Displaced soil forms the iconic anthills that surround subterranean nests.

contrast, polygynous colonies can lose a queen or two and still carry on with the remaining queens. Furthermore, polygynous colonies might on average produce a larger population of workers than monogynous colonies, with a larger number of reproductive individuals. However, polygynous colony formation presents a key challenge that likely explains its relative rarity among ants. The worker offspring of each queen are a part of different genetic lineages, which may give rise to a conflict of interest especially if different queens have varied traits in terms of number of workers produced or the ratio of workers to queens and males. These differences could lead to a breakdown in cooperation, as some lineages receive greater benefit from the polygynous arrangement and overtake and replace the other lineages, ultimately leading to a monogynous population. Thus, polygynous colony formation should only persist insofar as the mutual benefits outweigh the costs to some queen lineages.

vines that form a bridge between separate trees. As with polygyny, polydomous colony foundation carries the advantage of redundancy, such that the destruction of one nest does not entail the destruction of the entire colony. Polydomy also affords the ability to form larger colonies that may better exclude monodomous ants through direct competition or resource dominance. One great challenge faced by polydomous species relative to monodomous species is communication between workers as well as between queens and workers across the distributed colony (see "Castes in ants," page 94).

NEST RELOCATION

Nests built by a colony are usually stable over the lifetime of the colony, with perhaps some occasional expansion or adjustments made to the original nest. However, in some species, colonies are regularly relocated to new nest sites. This relocation can occur as frequently as four times a year in the Florida Harvester Ant *Pogonomyrmex badius* or even once every week in the myrmicine ant *Aphaenogaster araneoides*. Environmental stresses like massive rains or rising tides can force colony relocation to avoid drowning or other fatal risks. Outside of environment-induced relocation, moving nests likely helps ant species avoid predators who might otherwise learn and remember the location of stable ant nests, putting the survival of the colony at greater risk. Relocation may also increase the chance of finding new food resources, especially for species that do not forage large distances away from the nest. Interestingly, despite the competitiveness and aggressive territorial control of many ant species, current research suggests that the density of ant colonies does not drive nest relocation behavior.

There is variation across ant species in the number of discrete nests that make up a colony. Single-nest colonies are called monodomous, whereas those with multiple nests are called polydomous. On the ground, polydomous colonies are distributed across separate chambers or mounds that are not directly connected and rely primarily on chemical communication between nests for colony cohesion. A single *Formica* Wood Ant colony can consist of hundreds of separate nests. In the trees, such colonies often occupy a single tree, dispersed between branches, trunk sections, or constructed arboreal nests. A single arboreal polydomous colony in species like *Oecophylla* Weaver Ants can even occupy multiple trees, maintaining communication through touching branches or

NOMADS

In nomadic species such as the infamous Army Ants, colony foundation substantially differs from the typical form, as such species do not build true nests of any sort. While colonies may deploy temporary "bivouacs"—living tent-like structures formed out of worker bodies to protect the queen and brood—queens do not establish true nests. Army Ant queens, who are wingless, also do not participate in flying during nuptial flights but rather wait for the arrival of males that fly from other nomadic colonies into their existing colony (which can be monogynous or polygynous). How, then, are new colonies produced? These species evolved the remarkable alternative process of colony fission. After nomadic colonies grow in size, they eventually reach a size threshold after which they split in two or more groups. Based on chemical cues, different groups of workers associate with different newly produced unfertilized queens. Sometimes, the old queen or queens remain with a portion of the workers, but other times they are excluded. In this latter case, a different unfertilized queen heads each separate colony.

SEX DETERMINATION AND EUSOCIALITY

UNLIKE IN MAMMALS, WHERE SEX is determined based on typically discrete sex chromosomes, whether an ant egg becomes a male or a female is controlled by the queen. If she fertilizes an egg with a sperm stored in her spermatheca then the egg will develop into a female, whereas an unfertilized egg develops into a male. This process of sex determination is known as haplodiploidy and occurs in all Hymenoptera (bees, wasps, ants, and sawflies) as well as other species of insects, mites, nematodes, and rotifers. Females are diploid, meaning they have two sets of chromosomes, because they come from a fertilized egg and therefore inherit one set of chromosomes from each of their father and mother. Males are haploid, meaning they have one set of chromosomes inherited only from their mother. Beyond this consistent mechanism for sex determination based on the number of chromosome sets, ants have an extremely wide range in total number of chromosomes, from as few as one chromosome in the Australian Bulldog Ant *Myrmecia croslandi* up to as many as 60 chromosomes in the Neotropical Giant Amazonian Ant *Dinoponera lucida*.

In haplodiploid reproduction, a haploid male produces genetically identical sperm because the male only has a single set of chromosomes and thus genetic crossover does not occur. Assuming that a queen mated with a single male, all daughters inherit 100 percent of their father's chromosomes. This results in daughters that are 75 percent related to each other instead of 50 percent related as expected of sisters under diploid reproduction like in humans (where a random half of the genome from both the father and mother is contributed to each offspring). This high degree of relatedness among sisters—which form the workers in a colony—is proposed to be a mechanism by which eusociality evolved.

Eusociality describes a set of three primary behaviors that biologists consider the most complete form of sociality. First, adult individuals care for offspring other than their own. In the case of ants, workers care for the eggs, larvae, and pupae of the queen. Second, there are overlapping generations within a colony, meaning adults care for the next generation, which in turn, after reaching the adult stage, remains in the colony and cares for the following generation. Lastly, there is a reproductive division of labor, with egg-laying queens and with workers that are either sterile or otherwise forego reproduction. The fact that the haplodiploid reproductive system results in ant workers that are more related to each other than they would be to their own offspring, if they had any, may have allowed for the evolution of eusocial behavior where some adults spend time caring for the next generation of eggs rather than laying their own. Furthermore, full

LEFT: Even within the single genus of Bulldog Ants, diploid chromosome number varies across species from 1 to 32.

OPPOSITE TOP LEFT: When workers lay eggs, they are unfertilized and become haploid males. The fate of eggs laid by the queen depends on fertilization.

SEX DETERMINATION

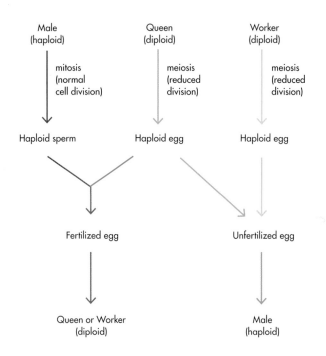

Male
(haploid)

↓ mitosis (normal cell division)

Haploid sperm

Queen
(diploid)

↓ meiosis (reduced division)

Haploid egg

Worker
(diploid)

↓ meiosis (reduced division)

Haploid egg

Fertilized egg

Unfertilized egg

↓

Queen or Worker
(diploid)

↓

Male
(haploid)

eusociality—with all three behaviors—could have evolved through intermediate stages. There are numerous such examples of intermediate sociality in Hymenoptera and other taxonomic groups. These intermediate types, classified as subsocial, communal, quasisocial, and semisocial, are each defined by some subset of eusocial behaviors. While eusociality may require multiple steps to evolve, it appears to be a strategy that often affords eusocial species with an adaptability and stability that leads to ecological success across a diversity of environments and habitats.

ABOVE RIGHT: Variation in chromosome number discovered within *Dinoponera lucida* populations may indicate recent cryptic (hidden) speciation.

RIGHT: The Neotropical Giant Amazonian Ant *Dinoponera lucida* has up to 60 chromosomes.

CASTES IN ANTS

DIVISION OF LABOR IS A HALLMARK of all eusocial species and especially so among the ants. Within a typical ant colony, the three major forms that serve distinct roles are called "castes." This term carries a different meaning than its usage in human culture and societies. In ants, castes are the reproductive female (the queen), reproductive males, and nonreproductive female workers. There can be further division of the general worker caste into subcastes. Such worker subcastes have different roles in the colony, including foraging, brood care, colony defense, and processing food items. Through evolving these task divisions among the worker caste, ant species can take advantage of a wider range of resources in the environment as well as better defend themselves against predators, competitors, or environmental stressors that might otherwise exclude them from some habitats.

The strict division between reproductive and nonreproductive castes is maintained through several mechanisms, which vary depending on the species. At the developmental stage, whether a female is an unfertilized queen or a worker is determined by both environmental and genetic factors. Historically, it was thought that nongenetic, environmental factors—such as the protein content of the diet fed to the brood—were the main determinants of caste (and worker subcaste) fate. However, recent research has demonstrated that genes play a strong role as well, at least in some species such as *Temnothorax longispinosus*. Once adults, the workers of some ant species, including those in the hyperdiverse genus *Pheidole*, are fully sterile, meaning they cannot lay eggs even in the absence of the queen. In most species, worker laying of viable unfertilized eggs is possible but suppressed through two main mechanisms: the release of pheromones by the queen, and a behavior called "worker policing."

Suppression of worker reproduction via queen pheromones is a clever mechanism that both ensures that produced offspring are the queen's alone and allows for some reproduction in the unfortunate event that the queen dies. When present, the fertile queen continues to release the chemicals that inhibit any egg laying by workers, which is overall effective but is limited based on colony size in polydomous colonies with multiple discrete nests. In such large colonies, workers in secondary nests where the queen is not present may encounter lower doses of the queen

RIGHT: The Florida Harvester Ant *Pogonomyrmex badius* is unique among North American Harvester Ants for its polymorphic worker subcaste. Here, only the smaller minor worker is shown.

pheromone, and thus are at higher risk of developing ovaries and beginning to lay eggs. This carries a cost for the colony, as workers that lay eggs have been shown to be less productive in carrying out other necessary tasks (such as brood care and foraging for food) than workers that are sterile. Furthermore, because the workers have not mated with males, all eggs laid by workers are unfertilized and thus, under the haplodiploid system, become males rather than workers or unfertilized

RIGHT: In apparent policing behavior, one *Odontoponera* worker aggressively grabs and drags her sister to prevent any rebellious egg-laying.

BELOW: *Formica* Wood Ant mounds are conspicuous features in some temperate forests.

queens. Yet this production of males could prove beneficial once the queen dies. After the queen's death, an ant colony with completely sterile workers loses all capacity to produce more workers, queens, and males, and thus is ecologically dead even if some workers continue living on for a while. However, when workers are not entirely sterile and can lay unfertilized eggs in the absence of queen pheromones, some genes from the colony can continue to be passed along to the next generation through male offspring, even if the colony is eventually doomed to die out without replacement of workers by the late queen.

BELOW: Dimorphism in the worker caste is quite extreme in *Pheidole megacephala* Big-Headed Ants, and the major worker subcaste certainly lives up to its common name.

WORKER POLICING

While the queen lives, some species utilize policing by workers to prevent unfertilized egg laying by fellow workers. This is a form of social coercion or punishment to prevent deviation from what is best for the entire colony. Workers engaging in policing will physically attack a worker that begins to express ovarian activity, which then triggers the suppression of such activity within the attacked worker. If such surveillance is insufficient and some unfertilized eggs are nevertheless laid by rogue nestmates, policing workers will even consume the eggs as food. Interestingly, there is evidence in the ponerine ant genus *Diacamma* that the intensity of worker policing corresponds to the reproductive stage of the colony. When small, before a full workforce has been produced, policing is at its most intense, which makes

sense considering that producing males instead of workers would be especially damaging to the fitness of the whole colony at this stage. Once the colony has reached full maturity, the negative impacts of worker-produced males is lower and may even positively increase relative genetic contributions by the colony to the next generation, and thus worker policing behavior is diminished. Lastly, recent research in the desert ant *Novomessor cockerelli* has also

ABOVE: *Cephalotes varians* Turtle Ants exploit division of worker labor by using soldiers with circular heads to defend the nest while smaller minor workers forage for pollen.

RIGHT: The heads of soldiers in some Turtle Ant species are not as perfectly matched to nest entrance shapes, and multiple individuals may be necessary to fully block a single opening.

ABOVE: An *Eciton burchellii* worker carries a large insect leg. Significant subdivision of the worker caste in Army Ants facilitates the transport of prey items varying wildly in shape.

suggested that rather than (or in addition to) direct policing, chemicals on the cuticle of larvae also act as reproduction suppressors. Workers disperse larvae throughout the nests within a polydomous colony, and so this behavior may also prevent worker reproduction in such large colonies.

POLYMORPHISM

Of course, workers have many roles within a colony beyond simply policing fellow worker reproduction. A single worker can, throughout its life, attend to various tasks, ranging from care for the queen and brood tending, to colony defense, nest repair, and foraging for food—it is often the oldest workers that leave the nest to forage. In some cases, species produce discrete worker subcastes with physical differences in size

and shape that correspond to their different roles. This is called "polymorphism," with the particular (and most common) case of only two worker subcastes called "dimorphism." In numerous polymorphic or dimorphic species, some larger and more aggressive workers act as soldiers both within and outside the nest, while their smaller sisters take on foraging and brood care. Soldiers typically have very big heads compared to workers, who can store more muscles to support stronger mandibles or perhaps to appear more threatening to competitors or predators. The African Big-Headed Ant *Pheidole megacephala*, as both the common and Latin names suggest, is one iconic example of worker dimorphism. Sometimes, such as in *Cephalotes* Turtle Ants, the soldier subcaste is defensive rather than offensive, blocking hostile entrance into the nest using their bodies.

In species with either specialized or varied diets, producing a polymorphic worker caste facilitates the consumption of a wider range of food types—including food items that are usually challenging to successfully access—compared to monomorphic (single-form) species. Even though each subcaste may be more specialized to certain tasks and thus unable to flexibly perform as many tasks as workers of monomorphic species, a polymorphic workforce can overcome this disadvantage through diet breadth or special efficiency in utilizing one type of food resource. The worker caste in *Eciton* Army Ants is highly polymorphic, which directly confers the ability of Army Ant colonies to consume or carry a very wide range of prey items. At the other end of the spectrum, *Atta* Leafcutter Ants have a specialized (narrow) diet that requires

growing fungus fed with mulched leaves that workers must find, cut, collect, and carry back to their nest. But like the Army Ants, these species also have a highly polymorphic worker caste, because the acquisition of leaves and successful growing of fungus require subcastes that are well adapted to very different yet equally necessary roles. A potential challenge for polymorphic colonies is lower redundancy within each subcaste, so the loss of a single worker may have a larger negative impact than for monomorphic colonies. Polymorphic colonies may also experience energetic loss or waste if, for example, too many soldiers are produced relative to foraging workers.

BELOW: The extent of division of labor in Leafcutter Ants may be unmatched. Workers that cut leaves differ from those that carry the haul back to the nest.

BELOW RIGHT: *Formica* Wood Ant workers can be polymorphic but do not produce discrete worker subcastes. They often forage as individuals.

WORKER EXPLOITATION

IT IS CHALLENGING FOR a queen to successfully mate, found a colony, and produce workers that can efficiently forage for food from the surrounding environment. A few ant species have therefore evolved alternative ways to develop (called "life history strategies") that exploit this work conducted by colonies of other species to minimize or even entirely avoid using their own worker caste for the work. This exploitative behavior, called social parasitism, can take several forms.

Kidnapper Ants are one main category of social parasite. Among the most iconic Kidnapper Ants, such as *Polyergus* species that raid *Formica* nests, queens still found their own nest and produce workers, but these workers are exclusively soldiers that are unable to forage for food. Instead, these

soldiers are specialized in raiding the nests of other species and carrying captured brood from raided nests back to their own nest, subsequently raising them as their own. When the captured brood emerge from their cocoons, they proceed to conduct brood care and foraging, unaware that all their labor is serving another species's colony. In some Kidnapper Ant species like *Formica sanguinea*, the workers can also conduct all the regular tasks of a typical worker, when necessary, but sometimes utilize kidnapping behavior to increase the success of their colony. In both cases, the energy involved in maintaining an aggressive soldier worker caste is outweighed by the benefit of avoiding production of a foraging worker caste, while the queen of the Kidnapper Ant species still bears the cost of colony foundation.

LEFT: During a raid, this *Polyergus mexicanus* Kidnapper Ant carries a raided *Formica subsericea* brood that will later emerge and unwittingly work for its captors.

While species that have evolved such a parasitic approach receive the benefits of exploited labor, they are also presented with a challenge. Within a given environment, the more aggressive or successful a Kidnapper Ant species is, the less successful host colonies are, as their reproductive output is lower or even completely eliminated by the parasitic species. This results in a smaller population of the next generation of potential host species, which in turn means that Kidnapper Ant species have fewer options for exploitation. Such a dynamic could ultimately limit the aggressiveness or efficiency of Kidnapper Ant species that must maintain a potential host population sufficient for the parasite species to avoid being driven to extinction. The ultimate reliance of socially parasitic species on their host species is likely one important factor in why such a life history strategy is found in only a small minority of ant species, despite independently evolving several times.

Other Kidnapper Ant species have evolved ways to avoid even the cost of colony foundation. In these cases, for example *Temnothorax kraussei*, the queen will attack and kill the host queen, and either take on the unique exoskeletal chemical signature of the host colony or innately express chemicals that are not recognized as foreign by the host workers. When successful, the workers of the host colony are deceived into thinking their queen is still alive and continue working to care for the infiltrating queen and any brood—including her own workers—she produces. The most so-called "degenerate" forms of Kidnapper Ant species, including *Temnothorax brunneus*, consist of a single queen with no workers at all. By usurping the queen of a host colony, the degenerate Kidnapper Ant secures lifelong protection and care by workers produced by another queen, including care for her offspring, which are exclusively unfertilized queens and males.

OPPOSITE: Reddish *Polyergus mexicanus* Kidnapper Ants with their host *Formica argentea* Silver Field Ants.

RIGHT: A socially parasitic *Temnothorax americanus* colony (dark brown) with a worker of the parasitized species, *T. curvispinosus*.

MYSTRIUM

SUBFAMILY:	Amblyoponinae
DIVERSITY:	14 species
DISTRIBUTION:	Afrotropics, Australasia, and Indomalaya
HABITAT:	Forest
NEST:	Ground-nesting. In rotting logs, under stones.
DIET:	Predators

MYSTRIUM ARE SMALL snap-jaw ants living cryptically on the ground and in leaf litter. Little is known about their ecology except for their predatory behavior as specialist centipede hunters.

QUEENS WITHOUT WINGS

Usually a winged queen flies the parental nest, mates, and starts an independent colony. In many species of *Mystrium*, new colonies are created by colony fission, sometimes called budding. In this scenario multiple individuals bud off from the nest by walking short distances to found a new colony.

Different *Mystrium* species can variously have winged queens, ergatoid queens, or intercastes. Ergatoid queens—wingless reproductive females—are smaller than workers with a reduced thorax size because they lack flight muscles. They have a functional spermatheca and ovaries for egg production. In the species *M. "red,"* multiple ergatoid queens are found in a colony. They can reproduce and care for the brood, but due to their small body and reduced mandible size they cannot forage outside the nest. *M. mysticum* and *M. oberthueri* also have ergatoid queens who all have the potential to produce offspring, but active reproduction is only seen in a few individuals per colony. *M. rogeri* has normal workers and winged queens but also an intercaste that has characteristics of both. Intercastes can lay eggs and act as reproductive members of the colony, yet unlike ergatoid or winged queens they also have the capacity to fight and are involved in colony defense.

DISTINCTIVE FEEDING HABIT
Mystrium camillae are sometimes called Dracula Ants for their habit of larval hemolymph feeding (see *Stigmatomma* profile on page 104 for details of this behavior).

STIGMATOMMA
Dracula Ants

FOUND GLOBALLY IN HUMID forests, these medium-sized ants nest in the soil or under rotting logs. *Stigmatomma* hunt mainly underground and alone, meaning they have very small eyes or lack eyes completely. Despite their reduced vision, they are ferocious predators of soil arthropods, employing their elongated and multi-toothed mandibles. Many species are specialist hunters of soil centipedes, which can make up 80 percent of their diet.

GRISLY PARENTING

As suggested by their ghoulish name, this genus of ants has an unusual feeding habit. Queen ants, and occasionally other adults in the colony, perform larval hemolymph feeding (LHF). Only larvae can feed on captured prey items, with adults unable to consume solid food. A Dracula Ant feeding session begins with the adult stroking a larva's antennae. It then uses its specialized jaws to puncture the larva's abdomen. Once the hemolymph—the arthropod equivalent of blood—is flowing, the adult ant begins feeding. LHF is only performed on older larvae, with the same individuals being fed on repeatedly and developing distinctive Dracula-style scars consisting of two-point puncture marks on their abdomen. The process does not seem to do any long-term harm, as larvae go on to develop normally. This feeding behavior is found in ten other ant genera who do not all use a standard method of extracting hemolymph, with some species possessing a hemolymph tap, meaning no piercing of the body is required.

SUBFAMILY:	Amblyoponinae
DIVERSITY:	Over 50 species globally
DISTRIBUTION:	Found throughout North America and in some countries of Africa, Asia, and southern Europe
HABITAT:	Humid forests
NEST:	Ground-nesting. Especially in soil or rotting logs.
DIET:	Predatory, some species specializing in hunting centipedes

FEEDING TIME

A *Stigmatomma oregonense* worker ant feeds on a larva by puncturing the abdomen with its elongated mandibles in order to release the hemolymph.

ECITON
Army Ants

SUBFAMILY:	Dorylinae
DIVERSITY:	12 species
DISTRIBUTION:	Neotropics, northern Mexico to northern Argentina
HABITAT:	Forest, swamp, pasture
NEST:	Ground-nesting
DIET:	Generalist predators, often feeding on other ant species

ARMY ANTS REACH AN EXTREMELY large colony size of hundreds of thousands of individuals. New colonies are founded by fission. An unfertilized queen leaves the existing colony with half of the workers. The new colony receives males, who mate with the unfertilized female. A fertilized queen produces 14 million eggs during her lifetime.

BIVOUACKING BEHAVIOR

An Army Ant colony has two distinct phases: statary and nomadic. In *Eciton burchellii*, the statary phase lasts around 20 days and the nomadic phase 14 days. In the statary phase, a temporary nest, a bivouac, is occupied for a short period of time with no emigration to new nest sites. The bivouac is created from the bodies of workers hanging together by their legs. Bivouacs may be established in open areas or inside existing cavities such as logs or abandoned animal burrows. In the statary phase, a single mated queen lays eggs and there are occasional foraging raids. In the nomadic phase, egg-laying stops, the colony goes on daily foraging raids, and those raids eventually turn into colony emigration. Foraging raids occur above or below ground, usually in a long column of ants but sometimes forming a front 30 ft (10 m) wide. Army Ants feed on many arthropods, including other ants. Most ant species will evacuate their nests in advance of an Army Ant raid, but some species, like Leafcutter *Atta* Ants, are ignored during raids.

DEFENSE MORPHOLOGY

Soldiers of *Eciton* ants are characterized by their enormous, fishhook-shaped mandibles, which are used as a defense against large predators.

FORMICA
Wood Ants

FOREST-DWELLING _FORMICA_, WOOD Ants, excavate underground chambers to form large soil-mound nests covered in thatch. The nests of the Red Wood Ant, _F. rufa_, are home to 22 myrmecophiles (species that rely on ants during part of their life cycle) and 70 opportunistic occupiers, including wasps, beetles, flies, and spiders. The Shining Guest Ant, _Formicoxenus nitidulus_, only lives inside _F. rufa_ nests. It is listed as one of 1,150 threatened species in the UK that are given priority status for conservation.

SOCIAL PARASITISM

Over half of _Formica_ species are social parasites. In the temporary social parasite _F. exsecta_, the queen invades nests of other _Formica_ species and kills the existing queen. Host workers raise her offspring until the colony is entirely composed of parasitic workers. In Kidnapper Ants like _F. sanguinea_, queens begin as temporary social parasites. Her parasitic workers conduct raids on neighboring ant colonies where they capture the host's offspring and return home with them. The kidnapped ants grow into adult workers that behave like the parasitic species. _F. talbotae_ is a workerless inquiline (permanent social parasite) found living in _F. obscuripes_ nests on the open prairies of North America. The inquiline queen is entirely dependent on the host, as she does not produce her own workers, only male and female reproductive offspring. She allows the host queen to live and lay eggs. Host worker ants provide all food and care for the parasite's brood.

SUBFAMILY:	Formicinae
DIVERSITY:	176 species
DISTRIBUTION:	Holarctic, all of Northern Hemisphere
HABITAT:	Woodland, forest, grassland
NEST:	Ground-nesting
DIET:	Omnivores

ACID REFLEX

Formica ants are able to squirt formic acid from their acidopore as a method of defense when disturbed.

OECOPHYLLA
Weaver Ants

SUBFAMILY:	Formicinae
DIVERSITY:	2 species, 12 subspecies
DISTRIBUTION:	Tropical and subtropical parts of Afrotropics, Australasia, and Indomalaya
HABITAT:	Forest and woodland, sometimes urban or agricultural areas
NEST:	Arboreal. Woven from leaves and silk.
DIET:	Omnivores

THERE ARE TWO SPECIES IN THE *Oecophylla* genus, each with distinct patterns of distribution. *O. longinoda* is found in Africa and *O. smaragdina* is found in India and parts of tropical Asia and Australasia. They feed on insects and tend honeydew-producing bugs. On citrus trees in Asia and cocoa in Africa, Weaver Ant colonies are used as a biological control in fruit orchards. They feed on insects that are crop pests, so their presence as a natural enemy helps prevent diseases transmitted by the pest insect species.

WAY TO WEAVE

Weaver Ants are named after the large nests they weave by binding together leaves using larval silk. A single colony, sometimes containing half a million individuals, can occupy multiple trees living in many discrete woven nests. To begin construction, minor workers hold leaves together, eventually pulling two edges into close proximity. Final instar larvae—those about to pupate—are retrieved from the colony. Major workers grasp a larva in their mandibles and hold it in position at the leaf edge. The worker vibrates its antennae around the larva's head, repeatedly stroking the leaf surface and touching the larva. The larva releases silk that attaches to the leaf surface. The worker then carries it across to the opposite leaf, forming a silk thread between the two edges. The process is repeated as the worker moves its larva from leaf to leaf, weaving the edges together with silk.

PROTEIN PROVIDER
Weaver Ant workers have a zingy lime flavor when licked and their larvae are widely eaten in Thailand as a high-protein food source.

MESSOR

ALL *MESSOR* ANTS ARE GRANIVOROUS, which means they feed on plant seeds. *Messor* are one of a small number of genera that exhibit all known ant foraging strategies (alongside *Camponotus*, *Polyrhachis*, and *Pogonomyrmex*), including solitary or group foraging and mass recruitment.

GOING IT ALONE

In solitary foraging, an individual worker leaves the nest and returns alone with food. The Asian species *M. aciculatus* locate their nests near neighboring colonies, meaning their foraging areas overlap. As solitary foragers, when these ants meet a hostile neighbor, they do not recruit nestmates, instead employing ritualized combat until one party retreats. In some cases, an ant that finds itself passing by a nest entrance will attack the residents and rob them of their seeds, even when they are being carried in the ant's mouth. Alternatively, they will enter a stranger's nest and steal stockpiled seeds.

The European species *M. capitatus* uses multiple approaches. They are normally individual foragers but will switch to group foraging 10 percent of the time. Group and mass recruitment foraging strategies use pheromones to recruit and direct colony members toward a food source. *M. barbarus* use permanently established "trunk trails" to forage. These trails of 3–100 ft (1–30 m) are cleared of vegetation and other debris. On 20 percent of paths, there are seed depots where seeds are dropped off by ants. Only a subset of seeds are harvested—they must weigh 4–50 mg and come from certain plant species.

SUBFAMILY:	Myrmicinae
DIVERSITY:	127 species
DISTRIBUTION:	Palearctic. Small number of species in Afrotropics and Indomalaya.
HABITAT:	Grassland, savannah, desert
NEST:	Ground-nesting
DIET:	Granivores

WORKERS' TEETH

Messor ants display large variation in the number of teeth on their mandibles. Smaller workers can have up to 15 teeth, while larger workers may have smooth toothless mandibles.

DINOPONERA
Giant Amazonian Ants

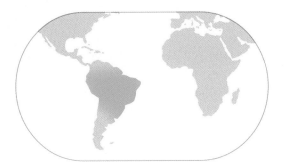

SUBFAMILY:	Ponerinae
DIVERSITY:	8 species and 2 subspecies
DISTRIBUTION:	Neotropical, including Argentina, Bolivia, Brazil, Colombia, Ecuador, Guyana, Paraguay, Peru, Uruguay
HABITAT:	Lowland and montane rainforest, savannah
NEST:	Ground-nesting. Multi-chambered soil nests.
DIET:	Omnivore. Mainly scavenges invertebrates and occasionally live prey, seeds, and fruits.

DINOPONERA ARE EXTRAORDINARILY LARGE ants reaching over 1³/₁₆ in (3 cm) in length. Known commonly as Giant Amazonian Ants, they are the largest-bodied ant in the world. They are well studied because their large size makes them easy test subjects. They have a well-developed sting used in defense and live-prey capture with particularly potent venom. A sting to a human can cause pain lasting two days.

THE LOST QUEEN

Dinoponera have small colonies of 30 to 60 individuals. Instead of a specialized queen caste, they have a mated egg-laying worker—a gamergate. To obtain sperm to fertilize her eggs, a gamergate mates with a male and then bites off his gaster to free herself. Workers within a colony occupy a dominance hierarchy. At the top is the gamergate, an alpha, followed by a series of subordinate females ranked as beta, gamma, or delta. Subordinates do not mate but can produce unfertilized eggs without sperm. These eggs will become male but if they are discovered they will be eaten by the gamergate. Subordinate ranks compete to be the next alpha. The gamergate will "sting smear" competing females, who are then attacked by workers. Gamergate dominance is also maintained through behavior, including antennal boxing and biting and gaster rubbing and curling. As well as policing subordinate females, other workers complete the normal tasks of the colony such as finding food and raising young.

FORMIDABLE AGGRESSOR
Dinoponera species can occupy distinct territories. When they meet individuals from neighboring colonies, they will lock mandibles and fight for up to 30 minutes.

4 | BEHAVIOR

TRAILBLAZING WORK

THE SUCCESS OF AN ANT COLONY depends upon a queen finding a quality habitat for nesting and, once a colony is established, workers identifying the location of food and navigating back to their nest. Unlike nearly all known workers, alates (queens and males) have ocelli, which are three large simple eyes that form a triangular pattern at the top of the head. Due to their positioning, ocelli face skyward and are possibly used to aid in navigation during nuptial flights or colony foundation based on celestial or other distant cues, including the amount of sunlight, the direction of the horizon, or other such environmental signals. It has also been suggested that ocelli could be vestigial, meaning a trait that once had a function when it evolved but is now obsolete and in the process of becoming evolutionarily lost.

BELOW: Depending on the subfamily, different glands can produce the trail pheromones that underpin foraging behavior in most ant species.

RIGHT: Ocelli, seen here forming a triangular pattern at the top of the head, are conspicuous in queens and males yet serve uncertain functions.

ANT GLANDS

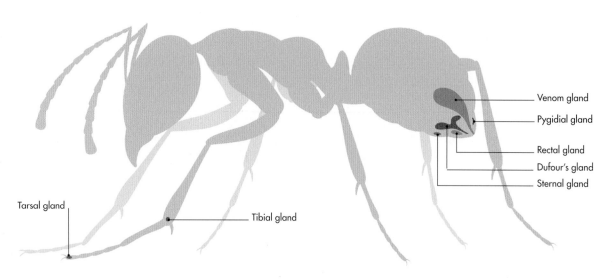

Venom gland

Pygidial gland

Rectal gland

Dufour's gland

Sternal gland

Tarsal gland

Tibial gland

If this is the case, then ocelli might have aided navigation in the wasp ancestors of the ants but are now unnecessary due to limited flight time for ant alates over the course of their lives.

FORAGING MECHANISMS

For most of a colony's life, queens are sequestered in the nest and the only navigational abilities that really matter are those of the workers. The primary task of workers venturing outside is to find food, and workers utilize several mechanisms to avoid getting lost during exploratory and food-collection trips. First and foremost among them is the pheromone trail. Most ant species administer special chemicals produced in various glands in the gaster, called exocrine glands, using their stinger (or acidopore or slit in the gaster). These unique chemicals are recognized by nestmates as trail pheromones. Glands that can serve this function vary across species but include the Dufour's gland (myrmicines), the poison gland (ponerines and myrmicines), the pygidial gland (ponerines, dorylines, and myrmicines), the rectal gland (formicines), and the sternal gland (ponerines, dorylines, myrmicines,

aneuretines, dolichoderines, and formicines). The tibial and tarsal glands, in the hind legs, are also occasionally used by some myrmicines. With the trail pheromones produced in these glands, workers can lay trails that connect food sources to the nest entrance.

Fellow worker recruitment to food resources is a decentralized rather than directed process. Initially, scouts leave the nest in random directions and begin to lay a trail either continuously by dragging the tip of their gaster or stinger along the ground, or in regular iterations laying dots of pheromone while walking along. Upon discovering food, and depending on the assessed food needs of the colony (see "Colony chatter," page 122), the scouts will reinforce the chemical trail on the return trip to the home nest. This trail reinforcement is important and a key component of the ant foraging communication and navigation system, because trail pheromones are relatively volatile and thus will evaporate quickly in the absence of reinforcement. Recruited workers, who typically blindly follow the trails laid by their sisters that

LEFT: Trap-Jaw Ants rely on their rapid and powerful mandibles to capture individual prey items rather than establishing recruitment trails to food sources.

preceded them, will disproportionately follow trails with a stronger chemical signal and will continue to reinforce the trail as the food source persists. Under this system, even without any leader ants or signposts, foraging workers will collectively "choose" which trail to follow among numerous options and, on average, forage for higher-quality resources. In some species, workers forage individually rather than collectively, but individual workers of these species still lay pheromone trails to ensure successful navigation to and from their nest.

Foraging via pheromone trails is an effective mechanism that takes advantage of eusociality (and thus evolved independently in termites, another terrestrial eusocial insect group). However, there are alternative foraging mechanisms, some that might represent the ancestral behavioral link between individual foraging and collective foraging using pheromone trails, and others that might have evolved out of necessity. In particular, tandem running relies on physical contact rather than chemical identification for navigation. Under the tandem running mechanism, a "leader" ant recruits a "follower" ant by using her mandibles to tug on her sister's mandibles and by presenting chemicals through her gaster to the follower. The follower then remains close behind the leader, tapping her antennae against the leader as the leader directs the follower to the food source. This behavior has been observed in Ponerinae (e.g., *Pachycondyla harpax*), Myrmicinae (e.g., *Cardiocondyla venustula*), and Formicinae (e.g., *Camponotus consobrinus*). Tandem running is also used by some of these species for nest relocation, even if foraging for food is conducted individually, for example in some predacious ponerine species.

OPPOSITE: For ants, accessing food sources many times the size of an individual ant is achieved through mass recruitment via pheromone trails.

ABOVE RIGHT: In the Sahara desert, the harsh sun and exposed substrate precludes the use of volatile trail pheromones.

ABOVE LEFT: Whether manipulating large leaves or subduing sizeable prey, Weaver Ants tackle big challenges using collective action.

In general, which foraging and navigation method an ant species utilizes may in part depend upon its main diet source. Collective recruitment is especially useful for foraging from large, immobile sources like a clump of sugar or a large decaying vertebrate, whereas individual foraging is sufficient for the capture of smaller, moving prey items like collembolan springtails. In environments where the high heat or exposure to the elements renders volatile trail pheromones unusable, such as on desert sand, alternative navigation mechanisms had to evolve. The Sahara Desert Ant *Cataglyphis bicolor* is one such example, having evolved unique spatially orienting ommatidia in their large compound eyes as well as the ability to count their steps to and from the nest.

COLONY CHATTER

AS CHEMICAL COMMUNICATION IS the glue that holds ant societies together, ants have naturally evolved refined systems for ensuring precise signaling and accurate interpretation of signals. Ants' paired antennae are the primary chemical receptor, functioning like a vertebrate nose or tongue, able to both remotely and through physical contact detect and identify friend versus foe, or food versus toxin. While walking, worker ants nearly continuously wave their antennae around, or tap nearby surfaces, including frantically tapping any ants that cross their path (which is termed "antennation"). Within the nest, this constant chemical and physical surveillance ensures that the nest structure is remaining stable and intact at all times, and most importantly serves to prevent any intruders from entering and remaining in the nest.

CHEMICAL SIGNALS

The colonial membership of individual ant workers is signaled through special chemicals on the surface of the cuticle called "cuticular hydrocarbons." These hydrocarbons allow ant workers to distinguish not only between their species and foreign ant species, but even between members of different colonies of the same species. When out foraging, if two workers encounter each other, they will briefly engage in antennation and, upon identifying that the other does not belong to their own nest, usually continue on their way. This behavior avoids confrontation that would benefit neither species, especially with neither food resources nor a nest to defend in that moment. When a colony is group foraging at a food source, however, dominance over the resource is often established in part through antennation and policing to keep

OPPOSITE: Two *Diacamma indicum* workers antennate each other, assessing the chemical identity of the other as communicated by their cuticular hydrocarbon signature.

ABOVE: Antennae are an ant's primary sensory organs, so antennal grooming is necessary hygiene for maintaining navigational abilities.

competitors out (see Chapter 5). Workers may also use antennation to determine how many workers from their own colony are at the food source and assess if further workers should be recruited. Antennae are so important for ants that they even have a special structure on their foreleg that acts like a comb and a brush, which they use to frequently "groom" themselves by dragging an antenna between the cleaning structure and their leg. Following this proper hygiene, the ants' antennae remain clean and free of debris, ready to detect cuticular hydrocarbons, pheromone trails, or any other chemical signal that emerges in the local environment.

SOUND SIGNALS

While most colonial communication is conducted with chemical signaling through receptors in the antennae, ants are also capable of detecting sound. Through a behavior called stridulation, ants produce vibrations either by rubbing their body or body parts against surfaces or by utilizing a specialized stridulatory organ. The stridulatory organ, which is only present in some ants, consists of two parts: the scraper, located at the rear end of the petiole (or postpetiole), and the file, located on the anterior end of the first segment of the gaster. By rubbing together the scraper and the file, ants with a stridulatory organ can produce "chirp" sounds that can just barely be detected by humans. Stridulatory vibrations and sounds are used by different ant species for different purposes. For example, in Leafcutter Ants, stridulation is deployed as a distress signal through ground vibration. If a worker is trapped by earth, fellow workers that detect the sounds propagating through the soil will begin digging to save their nestmate. This distress signaling through stridulation is found in many other ant species as well. Remarkably, research has also demonstrated that vibrations by Leafcutter Ants, produced as a worker cuts a leaf with a sawing motion, travel down through plant stems and can be detected as a foraging recruitment signal by nestmates who then arrive to carry leaf fragments back to the nest. In Harvester Ants, unfertilized queens and males stridulate as they emerge for nuptial flights, and mated queens use stridulation to inform pursuing males that they have already been mated. Stridulation is also sometimes used in concert with pheromone signals to indicate the location of a good food source. Ants can even respond to the stridulation of other insects, such as caterpillar mutualists, who appear to use stridulatory sounds to help their ant caretakers keep track of their location.

SPIT TAKES

IN ANT SOCIETIES, IF FOOD is not liquid at the source, then it will eventually be converted into a liquid form when consumed by a foraging worker. Moreover, most food collected by one forager is intended for the whole colony and thus will be shared with the whole colony. This sharing of food resources is facilitated by a special organ, the crop, which can store food after it has been initially consumed (though not entirely digested) by a forager. Ants have a separate organ, the proventriculus, that determines where consumed food goes—either to the crop for social digestion, or on to the midgut and the rest of the digestive tract for individual digestion. A forager with food in her crop can then exchange food with her sisters through "oral trophallaxis," a fancy term for "spitting in each other's mouths." Through oral trophallaxis, the food temporarily held by one adult worker is in fact available to be consumed by any other adult or larva; therefore, the collective set of crops among all members of the colony is sometimes called the "social stomach." When an ant wants to be fed from the crop of a fellow worker, she will tap her antennae and forelegs in characteristic ways against the mouthparts of her nestmate. Her nestmate will then regurgitate the stored food into her mouth.

A related social food-sharing behavior takes the form of excretions out of the anus, by either adults or larvae, that is then consumed by adult ants. This process is termed "oral-anal trophallaxis." Oral-anal trophallaxis, first discovered in the Turtle Ant *Cephalotes varians*, is used in some species to help distribute and replenish beneficial bacteria in the guts of adult workers, serving to maintain a healthy microbiome in the colony. In the Rapacious Panther Ant *Pachycondyla harpax*, larvae can digest food items better than adult workers. Through oral-anal trophallaxis, larvae can be used like little processing plants to transform food into anal droplets that workers consume to receive enhanced nutritional benefits.

Both oral trophallaxis and oral-anal trophallaxis may serve additional social functions, namely communicating important information or influencing decisions throughout the colony. Some Carpenter Ants can regulate the growth of larvae based on hormones passed through oral trophallaxis, and may exchange nestmate recognition chemicals through this process as well. Trophallaxis could also be a mechanism by which workers assess the quality of collected food, or how

OPPOSITE: Through oral trophallaxis, one *Formica obscuripes* Western Thatching Ant worker transfers food from her "social stomach" to her sister's digestive tract.

ABOVE: Research in Carpenter Ants suggests that trophallaxis promotes social immunity by distributing antimicrobial fluids among workers.

well fed the colony is, and accordingly adjust feeding behavior based on received signals. The Japanese Pavement Ant *Tetramorium tsushimae* uses oral trophallaxis to communicate information about which aphid species is a mutualist, even to workers that have not yet encountered aphids. Such communication may improve the efficiency of food collection from mutualist aphids by biasing foragers toward the aphid species that will actually provide food—when the "taught" foragers encounter mutualist aphids for the first time, they are less initially aggressive than those who were not taught.

SEEING IS BELIEVING

DUE TO THE DOMINANCE OF chemical communication (and sometimes stridulation) in ant communication, and the fact that many ant species are entirely blind, the role of vision in ants tends to receive less attention. However, some ants do respond to visual information for navigation as well as hunting prey and avoiding predators. Unfertilized queens and males, which typically must fly to a shared mating area or locate suitable nesting habitat, often have larger eyes than workers of the same species, corresponding to the increased importance of vision for the reproductive castes. Large eyes are also common among some predator ant species, who benefit from improved vision for identifying moving prey and navigating the environment while on the hunt. These and other species may also use large eyes to detect and avoid vertebrate predators. One such example is the arboreal formicine species *Gigantiops destructor*. Living up to its Latin genus name, meaning "giant eyes," this arboreal species is extremely difficult for myrmecologists to collect as it adeptly uses its humongous eyes—which consist of over 4,000 individual ommatidia—to detect any potentially threatening movements and dart away to safety. Recent research has even found that in Army Ants, genera that primarily forage underground have reduced eyes and reduced brain regions associated with eyesight, while at least some Army Ant species in the genus *Eciton*, who live mostly aboveground, have larger sight-associated brain regions.

Perhaps the most surprising finding about ant vision is that even some pheromone trail–laying species that forage collectively, and therefore might be expected to rely entirely on chemical signaling for navigation, continue to rely on eyesight to navigate their way. The importance of visual cues can even exceed that of chemical cues: researchers found that nest-relocating workers of *Temnothorax rugatulus* became highly disoriented when an artificial environmental surrounding was rotated. By contrast, the workers stayed on course when the surrounding was kept the same even if

ABOVE: Found throughout tropical South America, *Gigantiops destructor* boasts the largest eyes of all ants.

OPPOSITE: In many species, the nuptial flight is one activity for which vision is clearly important. Thus, queens and males tend to have larger eyes than workers.

the substrate underfoot, which had trail pheromones deposited, was rotated. Such a strong reliance on visual cues is additionally striking because workers of this species have relatively small eyes with only a few dozen ommatidia. Similarly, the Black Garden Ant *Lasius niger* uses visual landmarks and pheromone trails in about equal measure as guides to food sources. This kind of integration of visual landmarks and pheromone trail information may be common in ants as a mechanism to improve accuracy in navigation should either the surrounding environment or pheromone trail be disrupted.

LEFT: Recent research has complicated the prevailing view that ant navigation is overwhelmingly dominated by chemical cues, highlighting the underappreciated role of vision in ants.

SAFE AND SECURE

THE GLOBAL DOMINANCE AND conspicuous presence of ants in most terrestrial environments is a testament to their remarkable variation in defensive behaviors and protective morphological adaptations. Ants are well known for the ability of many species to deliver painful chemicals via a powerful stinger, but different subfamilies, genera, and species have evolved a panoply of mechanisms to protect the colony. In addition to the chemical stinger, ants utilize scissor-like mandibles, exoskeletal spines, and chemical sprays, as well as behavioral responses such as ground and aerial escape maneuvers, rapid swarming, and plugging nest entrances.

Many defensive responses rely on ant eusociality (Chapter 3) coupled with physical traits to achieve effective protection. Against vertebrate predators—including birds, lizards, frogs, salamanders, bears, pangolins, and other "myrmecophages"—individual traits like the stinger can certainly inflict pain even in isolation. Plus, in species where the sting of a single

worker may not induce much pain in a predator, the collective pain of hundreds or thousands of minor stings might. The true effectiveness of individual defensive traits, however, lies in learned predator behavior. Even if a handful of individual ants from the colony are killed by a myrmecophage, the predator learns via nasty experience to avoid would-be ant prey, thus conferring future protection on the rest of the colony. In this way, ant worker defensive traits are sometimes referred to as an "extended phenotype" of the reproductive queen, namely traits among nonreproductive workers with the primary purpose of defending the queen and her offspring rather than the life of workers. Ecologically speaking, a *Polyrhachis* Spiny Ant worker (Chapter 1) is akin to the thorn of a rosebush.

Ants also take direct advantage of their social connectivity to mount a rapid and robust response to external threats. Most species utilize special chemicals called alarm pheromones that, when deployed, may repel an attacker while also attracting additional nestmates to the area who upon arrival then join in attacking the intruder. Other species, such as *Cephalotes* Turtle Ants, have evolved a polymorphic worker caste with major workers (soldiers) that use their heads to plug up nest entrances while the queen, minor workers, and brood hide safely in the nest. Several *Camponotus* Carpenter Ants beat their gaster against the tunnel or chamber surfaces in trees, a behavior called "drumming," as a sound-based method to signal alarm that might be more efficient or effective than alarm pheromones in some contexts.

MUTUALIST DEFENSES

In numerous mutualist ant species, such as acacia plant mutualists in the genus *Pseudomyrmex*, highly aggressive collective defensive behaviors are used in service of defending non-ant mutualists that provide food or housing for the ants. In fact, this strong protection is the primary benefit received by non-ant mutualists like aphids and ant-plants. Avoiding

ABOVE: A *Formica rufa* colony mounts a robust defense by spraying formic acid. The chemical was first extracted and scientifically described from this species in 1671.

OPPOSITE: The Great Spotted Woodpecker, an omnivore that also eats beetles and spiders, shown here with a mouthful of ants.

RIGHT: The hardened cuticular spines of Spiny Ants like *Polyrhachis armata* likely serve as defenses against vertebrate predators.

the negative effects of herbivory or predation by outsourcing defense to aggressive ants is well worth the cost of providing honeydew or hollow thorns for the ant mutualists' colony.

AVOIDANCE

Individual rather than collective defensive approaches are present in some ant species. Such an approach usually takes the form of avoidant rather than aggressive behavior. Smaller, inconspicuous ants may have cuticle colors and shapes that serve as camouflage among the leaf litter or subterranean habitat—the widespread myrmicine genus *Strumigenys* often takes this approach. The foragers of arboreal species of *Polyrhachis* that do not have defensive cuticular spines may, when the leaf they are traversing is disturbed, quickly drop off the leaf and onto the ground to avoid capture. *Odontomachus* Trap-Jaw Ants display one of the more stunning individual-oriented defense mechanisms by using their hyper-powered, spring-loaded mandibles to propel themselves high into the air or some distance horizontally. This behavior increases the chance of survival of individual workers when they fall into antlion sand traps, but it may also serve a social defense function consistent with the majority of ant defensive techniques: when a nest is damaged by a vertebrate predator seeking ant larvae prey, a flurry of workers popping up and around may visually disorient or disturb the attacker and induce it to depart in frustration.

TOP LEFT: Camouflage and inconspicuous behavior rule the day for many *Cephalotes* Turtle Ant species.

LEFT: Hard wood surrounding nests may afford some protection for Carpenter Ants species like *Camponotus discolor.*

BUILDERS AND ARCHITECTS

THE ANTHILL IS ONE OF THE MOST recognizable structures built by any insect. Yet the simple mounds of displaced soil that form anthills lining cracks in urban and suburban sidewalks represent a tiny fraction of the diversity of ant nest architecture. Even the classic anthill mound is like a terrestrial iceberg: what is visible on the surface is connected to a much larger structure underground. Subterranean ant nests can reside just below the surface, or down into the earth as deep as 30 ft (9 m) from ground level. Aboveground nests in the leaf litter are sometimes constructed by loosely arranging the leaf litter substrate, or by co-opting a fallen rotting log, or even by occupying acorns. Some ants nest in crevices in tree bark, some under or between leaves, and some in giant carton nests between branches. In any habitat, one is liable to find ant colonies along the entire vertical gradient from deep in the soil up to the topmost regions of the tree canopy.

BELOW: Hidden below the surface, subterranean ant nests can include separate chambers for the queen and different stages of brood development.

AN ANTHILL

ABOVE: *Temnothorax curvispinosus* colonies are facultatively polydomous, utilizing multiple acorns or sticks when available, and more than 100 adult workers can fit inside a single acorn.

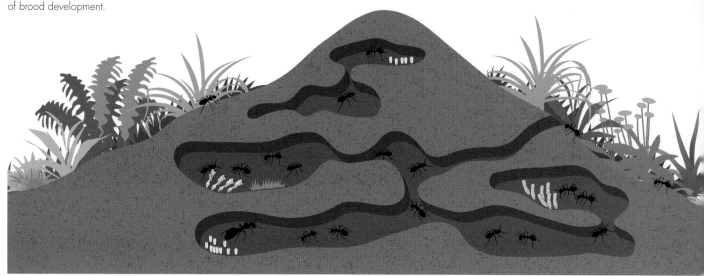

EXCAVATION

Excavating the amount of soil needed to build a subterranean nest as large as an *Atta* Leafcutter Ant nest—which can rival the size of a human home—requires an extraordinary effort of collective action. Initially, a small amount of soil is removed first by a mated queen, who digs a narrow tunnel attached to a simple chamber underground. In this chamber, the queen lays her first eggs. As the colony grows, more soil is removed, little by little, worker by worker, expanding existing chambers and forming new ones for more eggs, larvae, adults, and, in the case of Leafcutter Ants, mutualistic fungal gardens. Across many ant species, the characteristic ant mound is one solution to the problem of what to do with so much excavated soil. In addition to its convenience, depositing soil right by the nest entrance to form a mound or a turret may also protect the nest from intruders or accidental interlopers. However, these highly visible mounds could also attract myrmecophages, and it may be for this reason that several ant species instead disperse the soil at a greater distance from the site of excavation, rendering it difficult to locate the nest entrance.

ARBOREAL NESTS

Carpenter Ants are adept at excavating wood to form tunnels in tree trunks, leaving a pile of sawdust at the tree base. However, most arboreal ants do not take this approach but rather utilize pre-existing cavities (like beetle-bored twig cavities used by Turtle Ants) or create nest structures out of leaves or other available material. In groups like *Oecophylla* Weaver Ants and *Polyrhachis* Spiny Ants, nests are often created by binding leaves together with larval silk. While some workers grab on to and collectively pull separate leaves together or bring the sides of a single leaf together, other workers carry larvae and move them back and forth, the larvae excreting sticky silk like a glue gun. The final structure is a ball-shaped or dome-shaped chamber that can house brood, workers, and the queen. Alternatively, some arboreal ants build "carton" nests, which are globular structures consisting of various kinds of debris including soil, plant matter, and even animal poop. Creating carton nests may not require as much advanced social cooperation as is necessary to weave leaves together, but this benefit trades off with the necessity of finding and collecting substrate as building material for the carton nest.

AMBIENCE

Ant colonies are very sensitive to humidity and temperature, and both are therefore important factors in nest site selection as well as nest architecture. Mated queens of subterranean species tend to seek out moist soil or other substrate before digging a tunnel and building the initial nest chamber. A moist environment limits desiccation of the queen and her brood, helping the nascent colony preserve water. Some ants also adjust the amount of moisture in the soil to maintain a more consistent humidity throughout the different chambers of the nest. The Wood Ant species *Formica ulkei* is one species with such a demonstrated capability. It is not fully known how this humidity modification is achieved, but these ants may construct their nests in such a manner that

OPPOSITE: *Atta laevigata* Leafcutter Ant nests, one of which is excavated here, can include chambers reaching as deep as 23 ft (7 m) underground.

ABOVE: *Oecophylla* Weaver Ants are something like artisanal needleworkers, binding leaves together using copious amounts of larval silk.

structurally promotes optimal humidity. Several species preferentially place larvae in more moist chambers and cocoons in dryer chambers—the ponerine species *Prionopelta amabilis* takes the extreme step of lining the cocoon chambers with pupal cocoon fragments to dry out those chambers in their otherwise moist nests in fallen logs and rotting wood. The foragers of another ponerine species,

Neoponera villosa, carry water droplets from dew (or other available sources) back to their nest. After feeding any thirsty workers and larvae, the foragers use the excess for humidification by simply dropping it onto the soil within the nest or by dabbing some onto cocoons. Arboreal ants have fewer options to alter nest humidity, and thus many species have evolved a higher tolerance for lower-humidity environments, possibly due to properties of their cuticle or other internal mechanisms. The varied approaches deployed by ants to control nest humidity are a testament to the ecological selection pressures on all ant species to ensure sufficient moisture for the eggs, larvae, pupae, and queen.

MEMORY IN TIME

ANT NESTS ARE USUALLY STABLE in place over extended periods of time, and the average worker lives for a year or longer. With colonial lifespans that can reach decades, an ability to remember details about the surrounding environment and other relevant factors benefits the colony in the long run. Correspondingly, ant workers can have surprisingly good faculties for learning and memory given their small size and brains. Furthermore, learning and memory can extend to the social level, with social learning and memory leading to more efficient or successful colonial engagement with the environment.

As discussed above, the foragers of some species not only innately recognize chemical signals from pheromone trails laid by themselves and their sisters, but also recognize and remember visual landmarks that guide their travels. Ants can use the strategy of path integration to navigate, and this relies on short-term memory, long-term memory, and an ability to update information based on landmarks. Path integration involves mentally incorporating both the number of steps taken and the compass directions traveled into a vector that is used to orient the direction of travel. This process is initially implemented over the short term and can begin anew with each new trip outside the nest, but evidence also suggests that ants learn over time, combining vector information over multiple trips into an average vector that aids in optimizing the path of future trips.

Memories in ants can last days, months, or even years. Several studies on ant memory have been conducted with

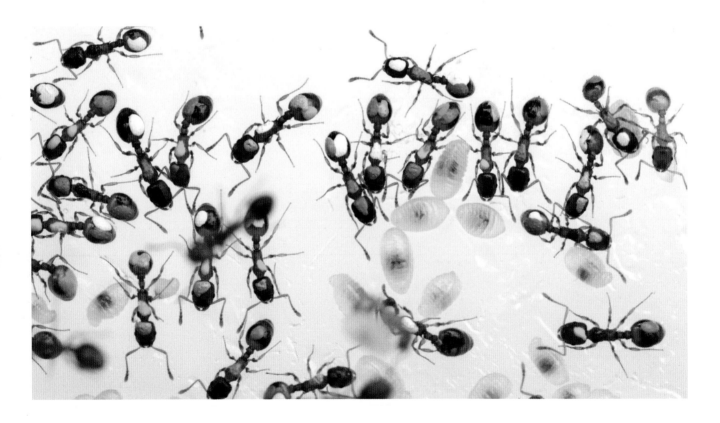

Wood Ants in the genus *Formica*. In experimental trials, *Formica fusca* very quickly learned odors associated with the presence of food and remembered this information for up to three days, even when introduced to the odor association just a single time. In a different Wood Ant species, *F. uralensis*, visual memory about site locations can persist even through six-month hibernation periods. When *F. rufa* foragers depart a newly discovered food source, they will turn back several times and face nearby landmarks, committing these to memory for future food site recognition. Cognitive abilities also appear to vary across workers within the same colony. In one study, most Wood Ant foragers could memorize the path to food when only a single forking path was involved, but when six forking paths were included, only a couple workers could successfully memorize the path.

How well ant species can remember spatial, visual, and chemical information may depend on the complexity of the environment and the method of worker recruitment that a species deploys. Naturally, more complex environments, like the varied and three-dimensional space of a tree, promote more advanced memory faculties. Ant species that rely on collective foraging methods may remember chemical information better, whereas species that rely on individual foraging might better remember visual information. Learning and memory in ants are generally directly tied to necessary tasks, especially foraging. These cognitive capacities are therefore often relatively limited compared to those of some other animals, like certain mammalian species that can, through more abstract reasoning, develop new solutions to new problems.

OPPOSITE: Painting ants with unique color patterns is a simple method for myrmecologists to track their movement and other activities during behavioral trials.

RIGHT: Memory is useful for ant species that benefit from relatively stable and valuable food sources like clusters of hemipteran mutualists providing honeydew.

CATAGLYPHIS

SUBFAMILY:	Formicinae
DIVERSITY:	99 species
DISTRIBUTION:	Central and North Africa, the Mediterranean, the Middle East, and Central Asia
HABITAT:	Arid and semi-arid environments, particularly desert and steppe
NEST:	Ground-nesting. Inconspicuous ground nests.
DIET:	Solitary scavengers and predators of arthropods

CATAGLYPHIS ANTS ARE THERMOPHILIC—heat-loving—and have adaptations to living in exceptionally hot and dry environments. One desert-dwelling species of *Cataglyphis*, the Saharan Silver Ant, forages in air temperatures of 113 °F (45 °C), while running on hot sand at 122 °F (50 °C). These ants have long legs to keep their body away from the hot ground and to help them run fast to cool down. *Cataglyphis* will make use of shadows or elevated points to find refuge from high temperatures. And many species have densely packed light-reflecting hairs on their body that form a solar heat shield.

NAVIGATING THE DESERT

Because surface temperature is high and food is scarce in the desert, *Cataglyphis* ants forage alone and do not leave pheromone trails to recruit other workers to a food source. They forage large distances using visual cues. These cues include using the panoramic skyline and surrounding landmarks through a process called path integration. They can also successfully move in a straight line even without any landmarks using distance and directional information recorded on the outbound trip. Distance is recorded using stride integration and optic flow perception. Directional information is recorded using celestial cues such as the polarization pattern, the position of the sun, and the spectral gradient. One species uses a magnetic compass to calibrate its visual compass when it leaves the nest for the first time before heading out on foraging trips.

REFLECTIVE HAIRS

Many *Cataglyphis* ant species have shiny hairs that reflect sunlight and help them to function in high desert temperatures.

COLOBOPSIS

COLOBOPSIS ARE A SMALL GENUS of forest-dwelling, herbivorous ants. In their larval stage they may be parasitized by mermithid nematodes. Instead of becoming reproductive adults, the infested individuals grow into an intercaste with characteristics between workers and reproductives. They have an enlarged gaster caused by the presence of the nematode.

EXPLODING ANTS

Colobopsis ants nest in trees, occupying cavities in live or dead plant tissue, where they have evolved a range of defensive strategies. Major workers are phragmotic, using their modified shield-like heads to block nest entrances. They act as guards and police who can enter and exit the nest. The ants modify nest entrances so they are a perfect fit with the phragmotic worker's head.

Found in the rainforests of Borneo, the aptly named *C. explodens* are also known as Exploding Ants. If threatened, minor workers will perform autothysis: they kill themselves to protect the colony. They do this by contracting their gaster until it bursts, sometimes wrapping themselves around an intruder before detonation. The explosion releases a chemical from an enlarged mandibular gland that runs the length of their body. This chemical is bright yellow, sticky with a strong unpleasant smell. The chemical sticks to attackers and a single ant can effectively kill or immobilize multiple attackers. Workers will perform this explosion to defend their nest or in one-to-one combat when away from the nest.

SUBFAMILY:	Formicinae
DIVERSITY:	95 species
DISTRIBUTION:	Southern United States to Central America, southern and central Palearctic, and Oriental and Australian regions. Absent from Afrotropics and most of Neotropics.
HABITAT:	Forest
NEST:	Arboreal. Nesting in cavities in dead branches or twigs.
DIET:	Herbivores

NO ENTRY!
Colobopsis impressa ants like this worker have abruptly truncated heads that are used to block nest entrances.

EUPRENOLEPIS

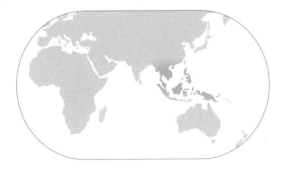

SUBFAMILY:	Formicinae
DIVERSITY:	8 species
DISTRIBUTION:	Indomalaya, mainly Borneo
HABITAT:	Forests
NEST:	Ground-nesting
DIET:	Herbivores

THIS SMALL FORMICINE GENUS is endemic to Southeast Asia, with many species recorded only in Borneo. These medium-sized ($\frac{1}{8}$–$\frac{1}{4}$ in or 3–6 mm) ants are found in tropical and subtropical rainforest where they forage cooperatively on the ground and in leaf litter. Colonies range in size from 500 to 5,000 individuals and may have a single or multiple queens. Some species are nomadic, nesting in pre-existing cavities and moving frequently, while other species construct soil nests and do not regularly emigrate to new nest sites. Most species are monomorphic, but major and minor workers are known for *Euprenolepis procera*, one of the best-studied species.

MUSHROOM HARVESTING

Fungus farming within ant nests is well documented, especially in attine ants of the Neotropics. Despite being an abundant food source, mushrooms are not eaten by most invertebrates because their nutrients are surrounded by a chitinous cell wall that is indigestible. Only one ant genus is known to harvest wild-growing mushrooms, a behavior recorded in the species *E. procera* and *E. wittei*. The two species live in the same forests but avoid clashing over food by being active at different times. *Euprenolepis* ants forage for many different mushrooms, dissecting the fruiting bodies into small pieces and taking them back to the nest. The mushroom piles are then processed by workers, who mash them up with their mandibles.

FUNGUS FEAST

Here, *Euprenolepis* workers are cutting pieces off a mushroom to transport to their nest. Once there, the workers will process and eat the mushroom pieces.

APHAENOGASTER

APHAENOGASTER ARE small- to medium-sized ants with an elongated body and long legs. They have a widespread distribution with diversity concentrated in the Northern Hemisphere, Asia, and Australasia. They nest on the ground in soil, under stones, or in rotting logs, with some species building distinctive funnel-shaped nests. *Aphaenogaster* are generalist omnivores and will scavenge for arthropods, tend sap-sucking insects, feed on seeds, and collect nectar. They are solitary foragers but sometimes recruit small numbers of nestmates to a food source using trail pheromones. They forage short distances but compensate for this by having a high nest density. Although they are highly abundant at food sources, they are behaviorally subordinate to other ant species and will not defend foraging territories.

TOOL USE IN APHAENOGASTER

Multiple birds and primates use tools for food transport, but it has only been observed in a few ant species, including ten species of *Aphaenogaster*. *Aphaenogaster* can only hold a small amount of liquid in their crop and do not use oral trophallaxis to share food with other colony members. Instead, they use tools. They drop items such as soil, leaves, or wood into liquid or soft food. This is absorbed into the tool and carried back to the nest where members of the colony feed on liquid extracted from the soaked item. Workers can transport ten times more liquid using an absorbent tool than they are able to carry in their crop.

SUBFAMILY:	Myrmicinae
DIVERSITY:	209 species
DISTRIBUTION:	Global, but lacking in Southern Hemisphere of Neotropics and Afrotropics
HABITAT:	Most habitat types in the regions they are found
NEST:	Ground-nesting
DIET:	Omnivores

EXTRA LENGTH
Although their overall size is fairly small, *Aphaenogaster* ants typically have long legs and antennae that give them a delicate, elongated appearance.

CEPHALOTES
Turtle Ants

SUBFAMILY:	Myrmicinae
DIVERSITY:	118 species
DISTRIBUTION:	Mainly Neotropics, Central and South America with a small number of US species
HABITAT:	Forest
NEST:	Arboreal
DIET:	Herbivores

CURIOUS FEATURES

Cephalotes workers possess an interesting combination of surface sculpture patterns, lumps, bumps, and spines, but the role of these are not well studied.

THE TURTLE ANTS, *CEPHALOTES*, ARE a tropical and subtropical forest species that nest in pre-existing plant cavities of trees, shrubs, and grass stems. They exhibit worker caste size dimorphism, featuring a phragmotic solider caste who use their enlarged heads to defensively block nest entrances.

FALLING WITH STYLE

Nesting high in the rainforest canopy, Turtle Ants can find themselves dislodged from their host tree. A fall from that height would equate to descending more than 3,000 times its own body length in less than ten seconds—the equivalent of a human falling around 3 mi (5 km). The impact of a fall will not kill the ant, but the hostile environment on the ground might. If the ant lands on leaf litter, there is a good chance it will be attacked and eaten by invertebrate predators, especially other ant species. More perilous is the chance of falling into water, where 42 percent of ants die, usually when they are eaten by fish.

To avoid the high risks associated with falling to the forest floor, *Cephalotes* employ a gliding technique known as directed aerial descent. They spread their legs out and hold them above their body like a free-falling skydiver and glide toward trees gaster first. Angling their legs forward and backward as well as moving their gaster tilts their body and helps adjust their speed, whereas asymmetric leg movements control their direction, allowing them to turn mid-flight.

MEGAPONERA
Matabele Ants

MEGAPONERA ANALIS, COMMONLY KNOWN as Matabele Ants, have large colonies of over 2,000 workers with a single flightless queen. They perform mass raids as specialized predators of termites in the subfamily Macrotermitinae. A scout will find a termite nest and then recruit up to 500 other workers for a raid. Raiders march in a long column toward the target termite nest for up to 165 ft (50 m). Larger workers physically break open the termite nest while smaller workers attack exposed termites. Termites are then collected up and ants return to their nests with the prey, a process often repeated up to four times a day.

SOMEBODY CALL AN AMBULANCE

Termites have evolved a specialized soldier caste to attack predators. This means workers are frequently injured during raids. Rather than being left to die, injured Matabele Ants are rescued by other workers and carried back to the safety of the nest. In a third of cases, injured ants die if they are not rescued. In cases of fatal injuries, such as removal of the head, thorax, or gaster, no rescue is attempted. Rescue behavior is a successful tactic, with virtually all rescued ants participating in subsequent raids. In 90 percent of cases where termites were clinging on to ant extremities, these are removed with no loss of limbs. And ants that lose a leg return to normal running speeds after 24 hours' recuperation in the nest.

SUBFAMILY:	Ponerinae
DIVERSITY:	Monotypic. 1 species but 5 recognized subspecies.
DISTRIBUTION:	Afrotropics
HABITAT:	Woodland, forest, swamp
NEST:	Ground-nesting. In termite mounds or rotting logs.
DIET:	Specialized predators of termites

IMPRESSIVE BOUNTY

After a successful raid, this *Megaponera analis* worker can be seen returning to the nest with many termites stacked in her mandibles.

PLECTROCTENA

SUBFAMILY:	Ponerinae
DIVERSITY:	16 species
DISTRIBUTION:	Sub-Saharan Africa
HABITAT:	Range of forest types, savannah, grassland
NEST:	Ground-nesting
DIET:	Predators, especially of millipedes, millipede eggs, and termites

THESE MEDIUM TO LARGE ants are readily identified by their long mandibles and shiny black head and body. They have small colonies of less than 300 workers where they nest in soil or rotting logs. For a small genus, they are widespread across sub-Saharan Africa and are found particularly in rainforest habitats of West and Central Africa.

MILLIPEDE MARAUDERS

Plectroctena ants will feed on many arthropods but mainly choose to hunt millipedes. Feeding on millipedes by larvae is a requirement to develop into winged females and workers, but is not an essential part of the larval diet to produce male ants. Queens in the process of founding colonies generally avoid large prey like millipedes and preferentially feed on much smaller arthropods like woodlice.

The size of the millipede determines the attack approach of the *Plectroctena* ants. For smaller millipedes, ants will grab the end of them from above, using their mandibles to catch hold of the millipede between segments. The ant is then able to sting it, resulting in immediate paralysis. For larger millipedes, the ant will grab the prey by an appendage and then proceed to sting or wrap itself around it, awaiting help from other worker ants. Experiments have shown that a single ant can bring down a millipede 94 to 117 times its own weight. In other cases, ants recruit nestmates to assist in bringing down their millipede prey.

FORMIDABLE MANDIBLES

Ants in this genus, such as this *Plectroctena mandibularis*, have long linear mandibles with one or two teeth that they can snap for defense or prey capture.

5 | ECOLOGY

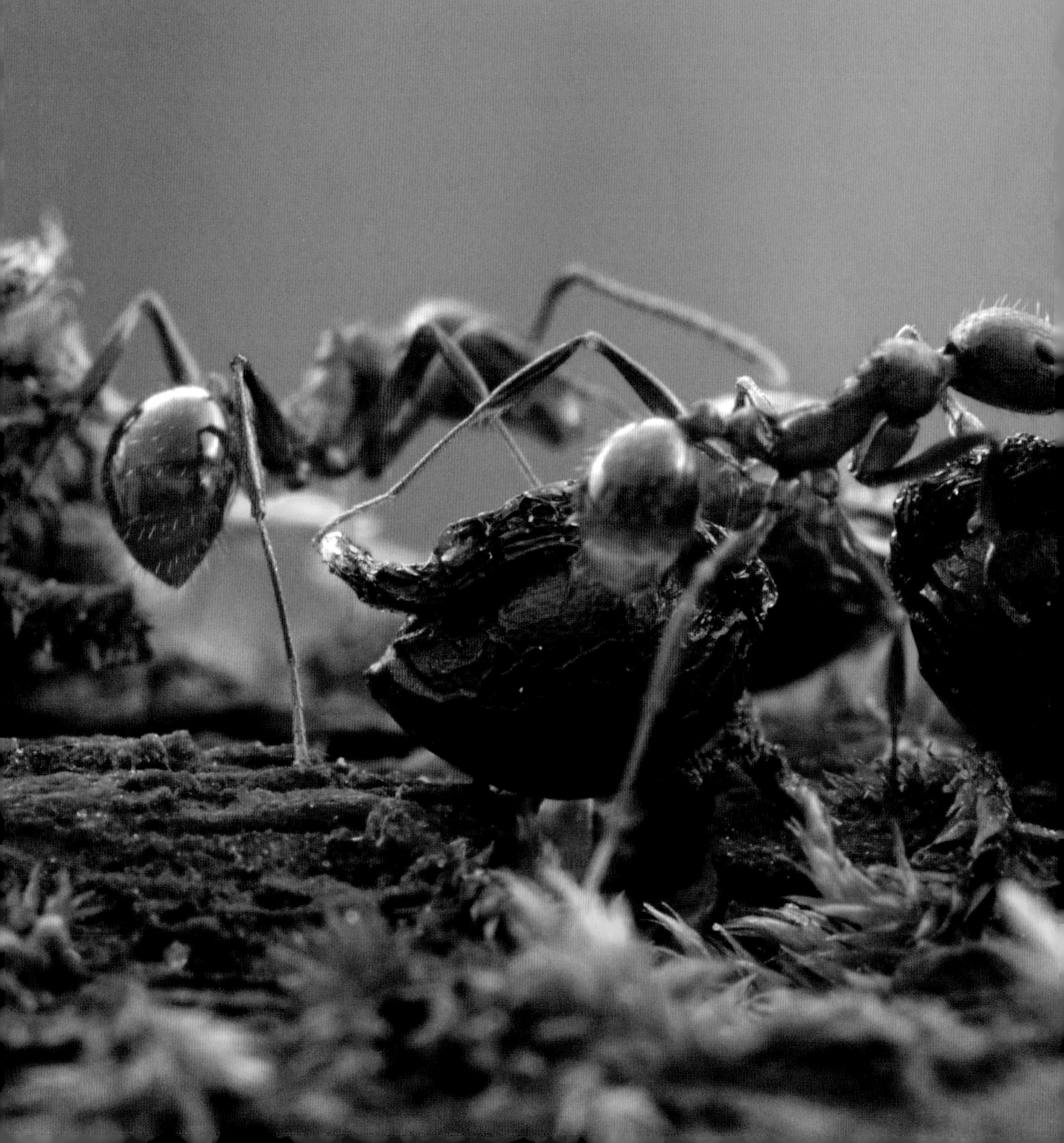

THE HALLMARK OF ANT ECOLOGY

ANTS ARE COMPETITIVE CREATURES. Antagonistic interactions between ants drive so many individual and collective ant behaviors that competition is known as the "hallmark of ant ecology." Notably, competition occurs not only between colonies of different species (interspecific competition) but also between colonies of the same species (intraspecific competition). An ant colony can expend substantial energetic resources to establish and maintain dominance over a territory or foraging location and remain vigilant against intruders seeking to take over their nesting site or food resources. Among less dominant species, foraging workers will constantly be on the lookout for dominant species, checking the "friend or foe" status of any ant that passes near their antennae (Chapter 4).

ANT WARFARE
Competitive interactions take many forms. In the most extreme case, ants conduct full-scale warfare. War among ants is frequently territorial, sustained, and vicious. When one *Oecophylla longinoda* Weaver Ant colony engages in

battle with another colony, individual workers and groups of workers face off in a frenzy of posturing, anntenating, biting, and tugging. As is a general rule, the victor is typically determined more by the number of workers than by the relative size of any one worker. Several workers can gang up on a single opponent and pin them down by biting and holding on to their legs and antennae, sometimes entirely cleaving through these appendages. Amid battle, a worker that finds herself temporarily idle will rush back to the main foraging trail of her colony, laying a pheromone trail along the way, and recruit more nestmates to the cause. Like for so many other behaviors, ants utilize the benefits of eusociality to their full effect to achieve domination over a competitor.

The Honeypot Ant *Myrmecocystus mimicus* represents a fascinating alternative to violent war as a mechanism to resolve territorial conflicts. At irregular intervals, colonies of this species will send out groups of workers from the nest, triggered by alarm-recruitment pheromones. When the group meets another group of workers from a different colony, they will initiate an unusual competitive tournament. Pairs of workers, one from each colony, will face off, sizing each other up as they make themselves look as big as they can by using their legs like stilts, raising their head up high, and inflating their gaster. Most of these tournament-style battles do not involve direct fighting or workers killing each other. This approach—nonviolent assessment of strength—may help each colony maintain a foraging territory while avoiding a lose-lose scenario where both colonies suffer the loss of an extraordinarily high number of workers (even if one colony ultimately wins a Pyrrhic victory). Such an unfortunate

LEFT: Three *Pheidole vafra* workers group up to defeat an *Acromyrmex disciger* Leafcutter Ant worker, vying for a delicious cookie bait.

OPPOSITE: With legs like stilts, Honeypot Ants engage in ritualistic one-on-one tournaments to nonviolently resolve territorial disputes.

scenario would disadvantage the species overall relative to other ant species in the community, and so the forces of natural selection may have favored more mutually beneficial intraspecific competitive interactions in populations of this species. However, even *M. mimicus* is not altogether peaceful. In a small minority of cases, when one colony determines that they are much larger than another, the stronger colony will initiate a raid of the weaker colony, kill the queen, and cart off its brood in an instance of kidnapping behavior (Chapter 3).

NEST DEFENSE

Nesting sites, a fundamentally important resource for ants, are also the target of ant competition. The disk-shaped or plug-shaped heads of soldiers like those found in *Cephalotes*

Turtle Ants or *Colobopsis* species appear to primarily serve as a defense against usurpation by other ants looking to invade their arboreal nest sites in twigs. The evolution of a soldier worker subcaste that is entirely behaviorally and morphologically committed to nest defense is reflective of the fact that nest sites are a limited resource for ants living in trees. Because failure to find and maintain a nesting site entails colony death, nest site limitation increases the likelihood of competition and, by extension, the ecological pressure on ant species to evolve ways to outcompete other species in the local ant community.

Potential nesting sites are generally more abundant on and below the ground when compared to trees. It may therefore be expected that relative to arboreal habitats, competition in

TOP LEFT: Specialized nest defense behavior in Turtle Ants protects against other ants looking to oust a colony in search of a new nesting site.

BOTTOM LEFT: *Dinomyrmex gigas* Giant Forest Ant major workers (soldiers) from different colonies battle by "boxing" each other with their front legs.

ABOVE: *Temnothorax rugatulus* is generally found nesting in relatively scarce preformed crevices in rocks, a preference that drives nest-site competition between colonies.

terrestrial habitats more often targets foraging territory and food resources rather than nest sites. Many ground-nesting species do indeed nest within a mere yard of one another, consistent with this expectation. However, the strength of nest site competition could be variable and depend upon the preferred nesting substrate of terrestrial ant species. The myrmicine species *Temnothorax rugatulus*, for example, often nests in preformed crevices in rocks, a scarcer resource compared to spaces available to more generalist ground nesters. Correspondingly, nest site competition has been demonstrated to play an important role in the behavior of this species.

INDIRECT COMPETITION

Ant competition is not restricted to direct engagement but can also take the form of so-called indirect competition. Indirect competition refers to situations where the use of a resource by one species negatively impacts another species in the absence of direct conflict between the species. For example, two ant species that are both termite predators might experience indirect competition between each other when the consumption of termites by one species leaves an insufficient number of termite prey for the second species, ultimately reducing the population size of the second species. An interesting case of indirect competition occurs in an Arizonan desert, not between two ant species but rather between seed-eating ants and seed-eating rodents. Due to limited seed resources, local ant species eating seeds reduce the number of seeds available to rodents, which in turn limits the number of rodents in the area. Similarly, rodents have the same impact on the ants. Thus, in experiments, the population of ants increased when rodents were excluded, and vice versa. Such an interaction highlights that ant competition meaningfully affects not only other ants but also very distantly related animals in the ants' environment, with possible wide-ranging implications for the entire ecosystem.

FINDERS, KEEPERS . . . OR NOT?

CONSIDERING THE STRENGTH AND importance of ant competition in ant ecology, it might be surprising that a high number of species can coexist in a single habitat. In one tropical rainforest in Uganda, researchers found 37 different ant species in a single tree. Even highly disturbed urban ecosystems like Manhattan in New York are home to more than 40 ant species. As with the evolution of traits over an evolutionary timescale (Chapter 2), trade-off mechanisms could explain species coexistence.

Niche partitioning surely plays a big role in the maintenance of species diversity. A niche is defined as the specific set of resources (e.g., food and shelter) and environmental conditions (e.g., temperature and humidity) used by a species to successfully develop and reproduce. By evolving unique niches, different ant species may coexist without driving any other ant species to local extinction. In the case of 37 species living in a single tree, even with intense nest site competition between ant species that nest within similar components of a tree, it is likely that some species utilize different kinds of nest sites, with some nesting under bark, some nesting

within twigs, and some nesting on or between leaves. This niche partitioning minimizes competition between species for the same resources. Even if two different species utilize the same nesting resource, like preformed cavities in twigs, one species may more adeptly find one type of food while the other species may be better adapted to finding a different one, resulting in a balance where the weaknesses of a species relative to its competitor is offset by that species' strengths in other components of its niche. In the Florida Keys, both the Turtle Ant *Cephalotes varians* and the exotic Slender Twig Ant *Pseudomyrmex gracilis* nest in dead twigs. However, the diet of each ant is quite distinct: the Turtle Ant is a forager of pollen, whereas the Slender Twig Ant is a predator of other insects and sometimes also harvests honeydew secretions from hemipteran mutualists. These differences in diet could explain why these two species can coexist.

DISCOVERY OR DOMINANCE?

One major hypothesis proposed to explain ant species coexistence is called the discovery–dominance trade-off. Studied in many different ant species and communities, this hypothesis proposes that different foraging styles have evolved to avoid competition between species, resulting in a higher number of species supported within a single environment. Species that evolved toward the "discovery" side of the trade-off send out more scouts and therefore prioritize the efficient discovery of food resources. According to theoretical expectations, this investment should trade off with an ability to keep control of, or dominate, a resource once it is discovered. Species that evolved toward the "dominance" side of the trade-off, on the other hand, produce fewer scouts and take longer to find food. However, once they find food, dominant species are better able to maintain control of the food resource by preventing competitor ants from intruding and snatching some of the food. Such species may also be able to kick out more discovery-oriented species that initially found a food resource.

LEFT: Ants, such as *Formica subsericea*, compete for hemipteran mutualists like treehoppers, and the mutualists in turn compete for services from the ants.

OPPOSITE: *Pseudomyrmex gracilis*, exotic in the southeastern USA and Caribbean islands, nests inside dead, hollow twigs.

RIGHT: *Aphaenogaster rudis* carrying a plant bit, potentially for use as a tool to absorb and transport liquid food. Tool use by this species may confer a competitive advantage.

A good example of the discovery–dominance trade-off in action was identified among four highly invasive species: the Argentine Ant *Linepithema humile*, the Invasive Garden Ant *Lasius neglectus*, the Big-Headed Ant *Pheidole megacephala*, and the Little Fire Ant *Wasmannia auropunctata*. Using experimental lab trails, researchers showed that the Little Fire Ant, the most dominant of the four, was significantly slower at resource discovery and worker recruitment compared to the other three. Conversely, the Big-Headed Ant and the Argentine Ant were the two least dominant species but best at discovery of and recruitment to food resources. The Invasive Garden Ant demonstrated intermediate levels of dominance and expressed intermediate discovery and recruitment abilities. Of course, this kind of discovery–dominance relationship is found not only among these invasive species but also among native ant communities, like in Chiricahua Mountain woodland in Arizona or in Atlantic Forest in Mata de Santa Genebra, Brazil.

TOP: Bigger is not always better for ants, a fact demonstrated here by several *Tetramorium sericeiventre* workers subduing a large *Pheidole* soldier.

RIGHT: Australian *Iridomyrmex purpureus* Meat Ants are dominant over different species, but aggression between colonies of the same species may prevent the complete competitive exclusion of those other species from the local environment.

Recent evidence has cast doubt on the general applicability of the discovery–dominance hypothesis. For one, although the above example demonstrates the trade-off among invasive species, the relationship *between* invasive species and native species typically conflicts with discovery—dominance expectations, as invasive species both discover resources faster and dominate resources better than native ants. Furthermore, one meta-analysis found that the evidence for a clear discovery–dominance relationship is weak for most published studies, despite the use of the theory over decades of ant ecological research. Thus, niche partitioning and other factors may prove to play a bigger role than a discovery–dominance trade-off in maintaining ant diversity.

BELOW: Results from Bertelsmeier et al. (2015), showing that among four invasive species, as worker recruitment (dominance) increases, resource discovery speed decreases.

One factor that may significantly mediate the exclusion of less dominant species by species higher up on the dominance hierarchy is the fact that even ant colonies of the same species compete vigorously with each other. Colonies of the Australian Meat Ant *Iridomyrmex purpureus*, for example, exhibit increased aggression toward colonies of the same species as colony density increases. Such intraspecific competition entails that as very dominant species increase in population size—meaning the number of independent nests in an environment grows in number—the population growth of the species will increasingly slow down. In effect, the species becomes increasingly constrained by itself. The superb colonial communication and competitive abilities of ants may have driven the global spread and ecological domination of ants relative to many insect groups of comparable diversity, yet the very same factors may often prevent any one ant species from fully dominating another.

DISCOVERY–DOMINANCE TRADE-OFF

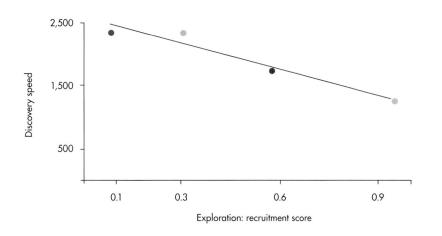

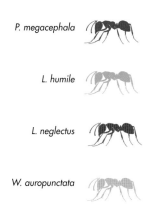

P. megacephala

L. humile

L. neglectus

W. auropunctata

SYMBIOTIC LIVING

IF COMPETITION IS THE HALLMARK of ant ecology, then symbiosis is close behind. Ants have evolved a diverse array of mutually beneficial relationships with both other insects and non-insect species as distantly related as plants and fungi. As a result of their species diversity and ecological success, ants are often the target of "commensalist" species that take advantage of ant behavior without negatively impacting the ants, and parasitic species that exploit ants to their detriment. The intricate complexity of these symbiotic relationships can lead to complicated species networks that may enhance ant species coexistence where they occur.

INSECTS

Perhaps the most widespread ant mutualism is the relationship between ants and sap-sucking insects in the insect order Hemiptera. Aphids are small insects that use their long and thin needle-like mouthparts to suck the sap out of plant phloem, one of the two nutrient transport arteries in plants. From phloem sap, aphids derive proteins but also ample amounts of carbohydrates (sugars). Due to the pressure from the phloem and the excess sugar in their food source, aphids excrete a sugary, sticky liquid called "honeydew"—essentially sugar poop. Ants, who often seek out carbohydrate-rich food sources, will harvest this honeydew from the aphids. In fact, many ant species tend aphids like livestock, protecting them from predators like ladybugs and moving their aphid herd to greener pastures when the plants the aphids feed on begin to wither. Workers will "milk" aphids by stroking them with their antennae, and they have even been observed bringing aphid eggs into their nest for safekeeping during cold winter months.

But aphids are not alone in being shepherded and milked by ants. Other hemipterans like scale insects and mealybugs similarly provide honeydew for ants in exchange for care, including anti-predator defense. Even the caterpillars of some species in the butterfly family Lycaenidae can produce

honeydew. These different honeydew-producing ant mutualist insects are all distributed globally, and therefore honeydew is part of many ant species' diets across various subfamilies. In some species, the relationship is an "obligate mutualism," meaning that the ants rely exclusively on their mutualists and their mutualists rely exclusively on them, each failing to survive in the absence of the other. The formicine ant *Acropyga epedana* engages in an obligate mutualism with *Rhizoecus colombiensis* mealybugs—during mating flights, unfertilized queens will even carry mealybugs between their mandibles to seed a new population upon founding a new nest. However, in most cases, such as in *Formica* Wood Ants, livestock ranching behavior serves as a "facultative mutualism." As with other facultative mutualisms, both the ants and the aphids can survive in the absence of the other, but they will engage in the mutualistic behavior when the opportunity presents itself.

TREES

An iconic case of obligate mutualism occurs among *Pseudomyrmex ferruginea* Acacia Ants. Like many other species in this genus, the Central American Acacia Ant has evolved a tight association with a handful of tree species in the genus *Vachellia* (formerly Acacia). These trees develop domatia, which are large, specialized hollow thorns that provide housing for *Pseudomyrmex* nests. Furthermore, *Vachellia* trees produce two special food sources for the ants: Beltian bodies, which are little detachable packages full of fat and sugar, and extrafloral nectaries, which are stem glands that secrete sweet nectar. With such a large energetic

CLOCKWISE FROM TOP LEFT: *Paratrechina longicornis* ants tending treehopper nymphs; *Lasius* ants tending aphids; *Meranoplus mucronatus* ants tending hemipteran nymphs; and *Technomyrmex* ants tending scale insects. A mutualistic relationship involving the provision of food, such as ant–hemipteran interactions, is called trophobiosis.

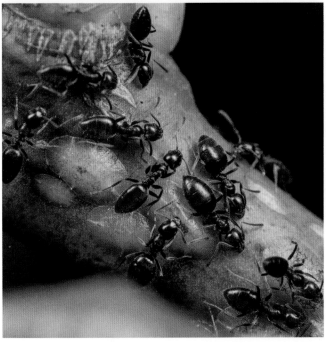

investment in supplying food and shelter, it is expected that the ants provide a large benefit for their host tree in return, and indeed they do. Workers in this species pack a powerful sting as well as a rapid colonial response to any vibration that could signal a nosy herbivore. The colony also clears out competitor plant species by regularly clipping seedlings that emerge near their host plant. This mutualism is an obligate relationship because, in the absence of *Pseudomyrmex* ants, the mutualist trees are overrun by competitor plants and herbivores and rarely, if ever, survive to reproduce.

Because of their mutualistic association with ants, *Vachellia* trees are called myrmecophytes, or "ant-plants." Worldwide, there are over 700 ant-plant species in over 100 different genera, a testament to the importance of ants across terrestrial ecological systems. These ant-plants are not all obligate mutualists. A common facultative ant-plant mutualism is myrmecochory, or seed dispersal by ants. Species in the myrmicine genus *Aphaenogaster* are common seed dispersers of myrmecochorous ant-plants in North

American hardwood forests. Like most ant seed dispersers, *Aphaenogaster* foragers are motivated to collect seeds due to the elaiosome—a fatty, protein-rich structure attached to seeds that ant-plants produce to reward ants for going through all the trouble of carrying their seeds back to the ants' nest. After removing the elaiosome, foragers will either discard the seed outside of the nest or deposit it into underground nest chambers that are dedicated to storing waste (middens). In return for producing the elaiosome, ant-plants can achieve a wider average dispersal, which carries the benefit of reducing competition with their own offspring that would otherwise result from dispersal at a closer distance. In addition, when discarded into a midden with other waste, seeds may find more nutritious soil amid the decaying organic material as well as a lower chance of predation by seed eaters, thereby increasing the likelihood of successful growth and reproduction.

FUNGI

Perhaps the most intricate mutualism of all is found among *Atta* Leafcutter Ants (and other closely related species in the attine tribe). Although their common name relates to plant leaves, these Leafcutter Ants form an obligate mutualism not with plants but with fungi. Workers maintain fungus farms in their large subterranean nests that are carefully constructed to maintain ideal temperature and humidity conditions for their fungal crop. The fungi are fed with a constant supply of leaves that are cut and returned to the nest through the coordinated foraging of up to hundreds of thousands of workers. Once inside the nest, leaves are mulched up by smaller workers, who then place strands of fungi onto the mulched substrate, which other workers will continue to monitor for healthy growth, including the removal of unwanted mold. The workers consume parts of the fungi as food for themselves while continuing to maintain and grow a stable fungal garden. Leaves are not normally a food resource that ants can consume, and so this obligate mutualism gives Leafcutter Ant species access to an abundant food resource that non-mutualist ant competitors cannot access, while the fungi receive consistent nutrition and shelter safe within a massive and well-defended ant nest.

OPPOSITE TOP: In exchange for providing ants with food, aphids receive defense against voracious predators such as ladybugs.

OPPOSITE BOTTOM: A *Formica francoeuri* Field Ant monitoring a *Lycaena xanthoides* Great Copper Butterfly caterpillar mutualist.

RIGHT: *Aphaenogaster fulva* foragers work to remove the delicious elaiosome attached to the *Sanguinaria canadensis* Bloodroot seed they dispersed.

NO HARM, NO FOUL

NUMEROUS NON-ANT INVERTEBRATE and vertebrate animal species have evolved symbiotic relationships with ants that benefit themselves but neither benefit nor harm the ants. This kind of symbiosis is called commensalism. Various ant behaviors provide opportunities for commensalist exploitation of excess space or discarded resources. By avoiding generating negative consequences for ant symbionts, commensalist species also avoid the costs associated with any anti-parasite countermeasures deployed by ants.

OUTSIDE THE NEST

The highly locally disruptive nomadic foraging trails of *Eciton* Army Ants have led to the rise of a remarkably diverse community of commensalist scavengers. Antbirds in the bird family Thamnophilidae include as many as 18 different species specialized in capturing invertebrates and even small vertebrates that flee from an Army Ant colony as it approaches and passes through a habitat. Some additional Antbird species facultatively forage for food through this

LEFT: Massive *Eciton rapax* Army Ant trails provide an opportunity for clandestine commensal organisms to hide away within the foraging column.

ABOVE: A *Phaenostictus mcleannani* Ocellated Antbird, an obligate follower of Army Ants, tracks the movements of a nomadic colony.

approach, even though they are not obligate ant followers like the specialist species, which brings the total number of Antbird species that follow Army Ants, at least some of the time, to over 200 different species. Other animals besides birds also engage in similar commensal symbioses with *Eciton* Army Ants as well as other genera of Army Ants. The silverfish *Malayatelura ponerophila*, for example, lives among the Southeast Asian Army Ant *Leptogenys distinguenda* and forages along with the nomadic colony. The silverfish avoids detection by masking its identity through rubbing against newly emerged Army Ant workers, taking on the unique scent of the colony.

LEFT: More than 100 mites hitch a ride on the gaster of a *Tetramorium tsushimae* Japanese Pavement Ant queen.

INSIDE THE NEST

Another common form of ant-associated commensalism is within the nest, where species live among the ants but engage in benign activities such as eating waste or mold. The woodlouse *Platyarthrus hoffmannseggii*, for example, eats ant poop and mildew. While this association is necessary for the woodlouse, which is rarely seen outside of ant nests, the association does not appear to impact the ant hosts and is therefore classified as obligate commensalism. Similarly, all species in the mite genus *Lemanniella* live inside ant nests, and at least one species, *Lemanniella minotauri*, has been observed eating black fungus growing on the wood in the nest of the host ant *Lasius brunneus*. A whole category of mites, called "phoretic" mites, are known to cling on to ants for the sole purpose of dispersal but do not otherwise appear to harm their ant hosts. However, it is possible that these and other generally commensal relationships can turn parasitic when the abundance of the non-ant species increases to such an extent that the ant colony begins experiencing negative effects like limitation of space, loss of food, or restricted movement.

ANT MIMICRY

Especially common among spiders, ant mimicry is a defense strategy that takes advantage of the strong defensive responses that ants often deploy. By closely mimicking the morphology, behavior, and sometimes even chemical profile of ants, ant mimics can benefit from the learned behavior of would-be predators that have learned to avoid the nasty experience of eating an aggressive ant, without expending the energetic costs of having to mount a similarly aggressive defense. Likely arising from the acute perceptive abilities of birds and other insectivores, ant-mimicking spiders often adhere quite strictly to ant-like morphology and behavior. This includes morphological adaptations like a significant constriction of the abdomen mirroring the characteristic petiole in true ants

(Chapter 1), and behavioral adaptations such as waving their front two legs around like antennae. Ant mimicry is likely neutral for the ant model species, although too many ant mimics in a local habitat could reduce the consistency of predators learning that ant-looking prey are dangerous, which could result in increased predation on true ants.

ABOVE LEFT: Ant-mimic spiders copy ant antennae by holding their front legs in a raised forward position.

ABOVE RIGHT: The golden pubescence, pinched abdomen, and overall shape of this ant-mimic spider closely matches *Polyrhachis illaudata*, below.

RIGHT: Well-armored *Polyrhachis illaudata* Spiny Ants are an appealing model for ant-mimic spiders.

PROWLING HUNTERS AND THE ENEMY WITHIN

ANTS CAN BE VORACIOUS PREDATORS—but they can also be prey. The number of myrmecophagous (ant-eating) animals is relatively small considering the ubiquity of ants, likely owing to their robust and varied anti-predator defensive traits (Chapter 4), but some species have managed to find ways around various ant defenses. Some other species also engage in the most antagonistic of symbioses, parasitism, with ants.

ANT EATERS

A number of large mammals are ant eaters. Ranging from Sloth Bears to pangolins to armadillos to echidnas, each is highly specialized to their unique ant (and sometimes termite) diets. The anteater, for example, has an extremely long nose and tongue that can successfully penetrate deep into anthills and sustain a diet of up to 30,000 ants in a single day. Because they have no teeth, anteaters rely on strong stomachs to further grind down consumed ants,

and they even ingest extra sand and pebbles to assist with digesting the tough prey. Interestingly, pangolins also consume small rocks and pebbles to aid in digestion, even though they independently evolved a myrmecophagous diet. Such extreme traits and behaviors demonstrate the difficulty of successfully capturing and consuming ants as prey.

Other predators of ants include some species of spiders (especially salticid Jumping Spiders), birds, snakes, Horned Lizards, frogs, antlions (among other insects), and humans (Chapter 6). Frogs are particularly effective myrmecophages, especially microhylid Narrow-Mouthed Frogs and dendrobatid Poison Dart Frogs. In these groups, more than 75 percent of a frog's diet can consist of ants, and several species are ant specialists. In fact, some of the most toxic Poison Dart Frogs not only successfully consume ants but also derive their deadly poison from the ants that they eat as prey. These frogs sequester chemicals called alkaloids that

RIGHT: With a rapid motion, a *Myrmeleon bore* antlion larva nabs the hind leg of an ant that has unwittingly wandered into an antlion sand trap.

the ants may use for pheromone trails or defense like in the stinger in some myrmicines or chemical sprays in formicines.

PARASITES AND PARASITOIDS

Ants must contend not only with various myrmecophages but also with threatening parasites and parasitoids. The case of social parasitism by other ants via kidnapping behavior and nest occupation was covered in Chapter 3. Parasitoid phorid flies often harass foraging ants, hovering above and then swooping down to try and lay their eggs inside workers. These flies are considered parasitoids, rather than strict parasites, because they eventually kill the host, whereas parasites

TOP LEFT: When ants detect decapitating phorid flies (like this *Apocephalus* species) flying above, they often move into an aggressive defensive posture.

LEFT: Ants produce chemicals, such as those in the pygidial gland, that parasitoid phorid flies use to locate potential hosts. These two flies arrived within mere minutes after a *Pheidole dentata* nest was exposed by the photographer.

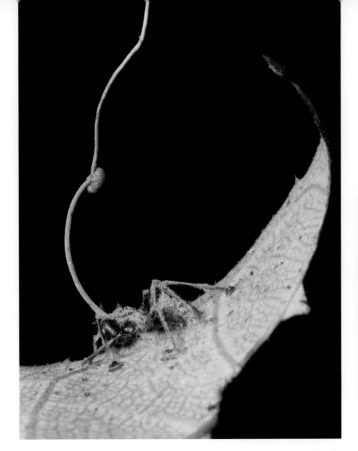

ABOVE: An ant infected with a mind-altering fungus grips firmly onto a leaf, its body eventually overtaken with the pathogen.

ABOVE RIGHT: The berry-red color of this *Cephalotes atratus* gaster is induced by a parasitic nematode looking to move into the digestive tract of a bird.

usually harm but do not kill the host. First, a pregnant female will use her long ovipositor to deposit an egg into an ant. Then, over time, the egg develops and hatches a larva that will slowly eat at the host ant from the inside while the ant is still alive. Eventually the larva will form a pupa, by which time the ant is typically dead, and then an adult fly will emerge from the ant carcass. In the case of *Pseudacteon* flies, or Ant-Decapitating Flies, the larva migrates to the head during an early stage of its development. Once there, the larva begins to consume the entire brain, and the ant eventually begins to wander mindlessly (literally). After a while, the larva releases an enzyme that decapitates the ant and continues its development inside the head capsule.

Mind-bending parasitoids of ants also come in the form of fungal pathogens. The process begins with an *Ophiocordyceps* spore landing on and infecting an unsuspecting tropical ant foraging on the forest floor or in the canopy. Over time, the fungus changes the behavior of the ant, causing it to wander away from the nest and use its mandibles to clamp on to a stem or a firm vein of a leaf. Slowly, the ant dies, while the fungus develops inside the ant, finally emerging as a fruiting body or bodies from which more fungal spores are produced and can spread to new hosts. In a related case with a different kind of pathogen, a parasitic nematode changes the color of a *Cephalotes atratus* Turtle Ant worker's gaster to a bright red. This color change deceives a bird into thinking the gaster is a delicious berry that it then consumes, facilitating the next cycle of the nematode's development.

ANTS IN THE ANTHROPOCENE

MYRMECOPHAGES AND PARASITES SUCH as anteaters, frogs, and phorid flies are undoubtedly formidable threats to ants, yet a single animal species impacts ant communities worldwide to a degree unmatched by any other species: *Homo sapiens*. Humans have so drastically transformed environments globally, resulting in major changes to the biodiversity and ecology of virtually all taxonomic groups, that scientists coined the term "Anthropocene" to describe the current geological age. Ants as a group can be remarkably resilient to ecological disturbance, but habitat loss driven by agricultural expansion and urbanization nevertheless significantly alters native ant communities.

LAND CONVERSION

The conversion of native habitat to agricultural land for crops or grazing produces an environment that is much less complex and thus provides fewer microhabitats and sources of food for ants. In Southeast Asia, the conversion of tropical rainforest into expansive rubber tree plantations reduces native ant diversity by as much as 30 percent or more. And

BELOW LEFT: Colonies of the Odorous House Ant *Tapinoma sessile* are small in natural habitats, but in human-disturbed environments they can balloon to more than 10,000 workers.

ABOVE: For omnivorous ant species with a flexible diet, discarded watermelons and other human food waste can support robust populations even in heavily disturbed suburban and urban environments.

OPPOSITE: *Oecophylla* Weaver Ants are aggressive predators of other insects, including crop pests. Some farmers thus relocate nests into tree plantations to improve crop productivity.

it is not only species diversity that is affected, but also species composition. When compared to comparatively heterogeneous rainforests in the same region, rubber plantation ant communities consist of more invasive species, more species uniformity between sites, and lower "functional diversity" (variation in species traits that serve ecological functions). Similarly, in the Brazilian Amazon rainforest, researchers found that, in addition to ant species richness declining along a gradient from pristine rainforest to highly disturbed pastoral land, both abundance and community complexity declined as well. Such findings demonstrate that agricultural habitats that maintain more complexity and native plant communities, as in shade-grown coffee plantations (Chapter 6), in turn maintain a more robust community of ants.

Urbanization exerts a significant impact on ants. Due to the habitat preferences and diet flexibility of many ant species, surprisingly species-rich ant communities can persist in even the world's most heavily disturbed city environments. In New York City, 44 medians host at least 13 different ant species and 11 different genera, and a potentially new species previously unknown in North America, affectionally dubbed the "ManhattAnt," was discovered on the median at 63rd Street and Broadway in 2012. However, the ecological flexibility of ants cannot entirely overcome the radical conversion of grasslands, wetlands, forests, and other native habitats into sprawling paved cities. Urbanization often promotes a decline in ant abundance relative to undisturbed environments, and cases where abundance instead increases are largely driven by non-native invasive species or the propagation of only a small subset of the total native ant species pool. In coastal California, runoff from nearby cities is associated with increased encroachment of native habitats by invasive *Linepithema humile* Argentine Ants that in turn homogenizes the local ant community as the single aggressive species displaces numerous native ant species. One study found that the urban ant community in Bogor, Indonesia, is largely supported by vegetated home gardens. While 94 ant species were recorded, 12 were invasive and just 2 of those, *Anoplolepis gracilipes* Yellow Crazy Ants and *Paratrchina longicornis* Longhorn Crazy Ants, dominated nearly every location. More on invasive species, including the role of climate change, is covered in Chapter 6.

CONSERVATION

Habitat conservation wherever possible may contribute to stem the threat that agricultural encroachment and urbanization pose to ecologically diverse ant communities, including rarer and more specialized species. Evidence suggests that urban parks, especially those with native vegetation, facilitate the conservation of native ground-dwelling ants in the threatened Cerrado biome in central Brazil. Native predacious ant species can also be manually "introduced" to agricultural lands as biological control agents that reduce crop pest populations. Research has shown that in coastal tropical dry forests along the Gulf of Mexico, isolated trees and small areas of regrown forests interspersed with agricultural lands can support some native ant diversity. Although these approaches are limited in their efficacy relative to large-scale conservation of native habitat, such as nature reserves, they may nevertheless limit the extinction of many ant species.

AZTECA

SUBFAMILY:	Dolichoderinae
DIVERSITY:	84 species
DISTRIBUTION:	Central and South America
HABITAT:	Forest
NEST:	Arboreal
DIET:	Omnivores

AZTECA ARE A SMALL GENUS OF dolichoderine ants that are generalist foragers who nest in live or dead wood, or construct carton nests in trees. Some species cultivate black yeasts, a slow-growing Chaetothyriales fungus. When a young queen ant leaves the parental colony, she carries the fungus in her mouth. Once she has established a new nest of her own inside a hollow stem, she begins growing small patches of the fungal culture, which she then feeds to her larvae.

PLANT PROTECTORS

Cecropia are fast-growing Neotropical trees. Three-quarters of *Cecropia* species are myrmecophytes, trees with specific adaptations to ensure the presence of mutualist ants. *Azteca* ants are frequent inhabitants of *Cecropia* trees, a relationship that evolved around 8 MYA. *Cecropia* possess domatia—specialized structures formed from the hollow cavities in the stems that ants can nest in. If any damage occurs to their domatia nests, *Azteca* ants will repair holes by patching them up with sap and plant fibers. To feed the ants, *Cecropia* grows Müllerian food bodies, glycogen-rich structures growing from the base of leaves. In return for food and housing, *Azteca* aggressively defend the trees against herbivore and pathogen attack, increase available nutrients, and prevent encroachment by removing nearby vegetation. *Cecropia* plants with *Azteca* ant colonies grow faster than those without ants; they have higher levels of nitrogen and experience lower levels of herbivory.

PROTECTIVE WORKERS
Azteca alfari workers in Panama. Despite their small size, they are aggressive defenders of their host *Cecropia* tree.

RHYTIDOPONERA

IF YOU STUMBLE UPON AN ANT in Australia, there is a good chance it will be a *Rhytidoponera*. These small to medium-sized ants have a heavily sculptured exoskeleton and sometimes metallic coloration. Occupying a range of natural habitats like woodland, scrub, and open arid regions, they are equally abundant in the urban settings of parks and gardens. Forest species will nest in trees, but most *Rhytidoponera* are soil-nesting, either under logs and stones or as mound builders. Nest location sites are chosen with care. *R. metallica* colonies avoid nesting under small rocks as this can limit colony growth. The larger the rock, the larger and more successful the colony.

SOWING THE SEED

Myrmecochorous plants are those dependent on ants for their dispersal. Their seeds have elaiosomes attached, specialized nutritious food bodies that tempt ants into collecting them. In temperate forests there are between 2 to 20 species of seed-dispersing ants, compared with hundreds of species in tropical forests. In Australia, *Rhytidoponera* act as a keystone mutualist, accounting for 45–72 percent of the seed dispersal for myrmecochorous plant species. Seeds are carried distances of 6–12 ft (1.8–3.8 m). Foraging for seeds is a seasonal activity that occurs one to four months after the main plant-flowering period. For *Rhytidoponera*, around 6 percent of their diet comes from seeds, with the rest made up of other prey or scavenged food like invertebrates or carrion.

SUBFAMILY:	Ectatomminae
DIVERSITY:	103 species
DISTRIBUTION:	Australasia and Indomalaya
HABITAT:	All habitat types found within their distribution. Common in disturbed areas and urban habitats.
NEST:	Ground-nesting. Rarely arboreal.
DIET:	Omnivores, granivores, predators

CHARACTERISTIC FEATURES
The metallic colors and strong surface sculpture of this worker are typical of ants in the *Rhytidoponera* genus.

ANOPLOLEPIS
Pugnacious Ants

SUBFAMILY:	Formicinae
DIVERSITY:	10 species
DISTRIBUTION:	Native range: Afrotropics and Indomalaya. Invasive: global.
HABITAT:	Forest, scrub, arid habitats, agricultural land
NEST:	Ground-nesting
DIET:	Omnivores

ALSO KNOWN AS PUGNACIOUS ANTS, this small genus is native to the Afrotropics except for one species found in Indomalaya. They are generalist predators and scavengers of invertebrates, honeydew, and nectar. *Anoplolepis* are fast-moving and aggressive ants, often being one of the dominant species in the areas they occupy.

CRAZY ANTS ON CHRISTMAS ISLAND

A. gracilipes, the Yellow Crazy Ant, was awarded the unfortunate accomplishment of being in the world's top 100 most invasive species. Native to Asia, it has now spread into other tropical and subtropical regions. In its invasive range it forms supercolonies where densities reach over 2,000 ants per 10 ft^2 (1 m^2) on the forest floor.

The impact of Yellow Crazy Ants has been severe on islands where native wildlife lack defenses to protect themselves. In Hawaii, Yellow Crazy Ants have displaced native *Tetragnatha* spiders, and in the Seychelles, they are responsible for the decline of the Seychelles' endemic Skink and Sooty Tern. On Christmas Island, they have invaded over a quarter of the island's rainforest, reducing populations and the nesting success of the Emerald Dove and Christmas Island Thrush. They overwhelm Red Land Crabs by spraying formic acid in their eyes and mouth, leading to death within 48 hours. The ants then eat the crabs and move into their burrows. An estimated 10–15 million Red Land Crabs, around one-third of the entire population, have been killed by ants.

TENDING HEMIPTERANS

An *Anoplolepis* worker ant tends hemipterans for their honeydew. This makes the genus a serious secondary pest in agricultural systems.

CAMPONOTUS
Carpenter Ants

THE HYPERDIVERSE GENUS OF *Camponotus* is found in virtually every country in the world, occupying a range of habitat types as generalist omnivores. While *Pheidole* ants currently hold the record for the most species-rich genus, a modern revision of *Camponotus* taxonomy could reveal it to be the largest ant genera. As well as being diverse, *Camponotus* are abundant, numerically dominant components of the places they inhabit. In primary forest in New Guinea, they account for 18 percent of all ant species and 20 percent of all nest sites, and are found occupying 20 percent of all trees. *Camponotus* have minor and major worker castes, with minors responsible for foraging and majors involved in colony defense, sometimes using phragmosis to block the nest entrance with their head.

TREE-NESTING CARPENTERS

Camponotus are easily spotted foraging for invertebrates, plant secretions, or honeydew. Many species nest on the ground but others occupy pre-existing cavities in trees, including those made by other insects. Arboreal nests take a range of forms and can be found in aerial soil, in dead or live tree branches or trunks, or inside liana stems. The name Carpenter Ants comes from their ability to excavate nests in wood. They are considered major pests when the wood is part of a building rather than a tree in a forest. Some *Camponotus* species are plant mutualists, providing defense in return for nesting space in specialized plant structures.

SUBFAMILY:	Formicinae
DIVERSITY:	1,089 species
DISTRIBUTION:	Found globally, except very northerly latitudes and some islands
HABITAT:	Virtually all habitats (and microhabitats)
NEST:	Usually ground-nesting. Sometimes arboreal.
DIET:	Omnivores

DIETARY BOOST

Camponotus ants host endosymbiotic bacteria, *Blochmannia*, that upgrade the diet of their host ants by providing them with essential amino acids.

ATTA
Leafcutter Ants

SUBFAMILY:	Myrmicinae
DIVERSITY:	15 species
DISTRIBUTION:	Neotropics
HABITAT:	Forest, Cerrado, agricultural or urban environments
NEST:	Ground-nesting. Sometimes very large nests.
DIET:	Herbivores

COMMUNICATION CHANNELS

Leafcutter Ants use vibrations that are transmitted through their bodies and then carried through plants to tell other workers to join in leaf cutting with them.

AS THE NAME SUGGESTS, LEAFCUTTER Ants harvest fresh leaves, especially young leaves that have higher nutrient and lower toxin content. They will also collect flowers, dried plant parts, seeds, and insect excrement, foraging up to 650 ft (200 m) from the nest. In Neotropical forests, they account for 25 percent of all herbivory, removing 10–15 percent of all the leaves within range of their nest. Around 5–15 MYA they evolved a symbiotic relationship with a fungus, which inside the nest breaks down the freshly harvested plant material into hyphal nodules the ants feed on.

ECOSYSTEM ENGINEERS

Leafcutter Ants are effective ecosystem engineers through their ability to alter the physical, chemical, and biological environment around their nests. They excavate large soil nests up to 840 ft^2 (78 m^2) in area and 25 ft (8 m) in depth. From a central nest area there can be up to 7,000 fungal chambers connected by foraging and ventilation tunnels. Environmental conditions in the nest (humidity, temperature, and gas concentrations) are regulated for optimal fungal growth and brood development. *Atta vollenweideri* change the height and number of ventilation turrets to manage levels of CO_2.

The process of nest creation changes soil aeration, density, water retention, and temperature, as well as mixes together nutrient-poor and -rich soil from different depths. Physical soil structure is changed as soil is rolled into pellets to create a less dense and more porous soil for better soil ventilation.

NEOPONERA

NEOPONERA ARE MEDIUM TO LARGE Neotropical ants that nest in soil, rotting wood, or trees. They are generalist predators and scavengers of live and dead insects, vertebrate carcasses, fruit, and nectar, as well as specialized predators of termites.

ANT GARDENS

Several tropical arboreal ant species create ant gardens, a carton (plant fiber) ant nest with epiphytic plants growing out of it. Multiple ant species can partner with various plant species. The most common inhabitants of ant gardens in Southeast Asia are *Crematogaster* species, whereas in the Neotropics the ants are frequently *Camponotus femoratus*, *Crematogaster levior*, and *Neoponera goeldii*. Queens of *N. goeldii* create an ant garden by first building a small carton nest on a leaf or branch. Epiphyte seeds are found, often from the droppings of vertebrates, and incorporated into the nest construction. The epiphytes then grow out of the nest, with ants continually replacing seeds and expanding the nest as the colony grows. *N. goeldii* colonies are polycalic—they occupy several nests, at times over multiple trees.

Ant gardens are beneficial to both parties. Ants provide the epiphytes with seed dispersal and increased nutrients. Ant nests are strengthened by the epiphyte roots and physically protected from rain by the plant leaves, a useful feature in a rainforest. Plants transpire water out of the carton to prevent the nest becoming waterlogged. Some epiphytes provide nectar, elaiosomes, and fruit pulp to ants.

SUBFAMILY:	Ponerinae
DIVERSITY:	56
DISTRIBUTION:	Neotropics, southern Texas to southern Brazil
HABITAT:	Scrub, forest, Cerrado, urban gardens
NEST:	Ground-nesting or arboreal
DIET:	Specialized termite hunters or generalist predators and omnivores

DISTINCTIVE FEATURES
Neoponera apicalis can be recognized by its large eyes, black body, the absence of erect hairs on the top of the mesosoma, and the yellow-tipped antennae.

TETRAPONERA

SUBFAMILY:	Pseudomyrmecinae
DIVERSITY:	87 species
DISTRIBUTION:	Afrotropics, Australasia, and Indomalaya
HABITAT:	Forest, woodland, savannah, mangrove
NEST:	Arboreal
DIET:	Omnivores and herbivores

TETRAPONERA ARE A PALEOTROPICAL and Australian genus of arboreal ants. They nest in dead branches or twigs, as well as domatia, specialized ant-housing structures. There are some omnivorous species but most are herbivores, feeding on the plant exudates or the honeydew of sap-sucking bugs. Herbivorous ants have a sugar-rich diet that lacks essential amino acids, leaving them short of nitrogen. To overcome this, some species have a pouch between the midgut and intestine that houses bacterial gut symbionts. The Rhizobiales bacteria living in the ant pouch likely have a role in nitrogen fixation and allow the ants to supplement their nitrogen-poor diet.

WHEN IS AN ANT NOT AN ANT?

Ant-mimicry, myrmecomorphy, is common in Jumping Spiders (Salticidae). These spiders modify their physical appearance and behavior to avoid attack by visually hunting predators, who see them as an unpalatable or aggressive ant species. The Southeast Asian Jumping Spider *Myrmarachne cornuta* mimics *Tetraponera* ants. Spiders have a constriction in the cephalothorax to create the appearance of a separate head and body as well as a lengthened pedicel and elongated abdomen. They also mimic ant behavior by moving erratically and lifting the first pair of legs to create the illusion of having antennae. The spider may avoid predation, but there is a cost. Due to its physical modifications, *M. cornuta* jumps shorter distances and has a lower rate of prey-capture success than its non-ant-mimicking counterparts.

TWIG ANT

Tetraponera are sometimes known as Twig Ants because their long, slender bodies are ideally suited to nest in hollow branches and twigs.

6 | ANTS AND PEOPLE

FARMING FRIEND OR FOE?

ANTS ARE FREQUENTLY "ECOSYSTEM engineers" that can transform their environment through nest construction and nutrient cycling in ways that affect the entire biological community. *Atta* Leafcutter Ants, featured in Chapter 5, represent a particularly influential group of ecosystem-engineering ants. Ants in agricultural ecosystems—or "agroecosystems"—are no exception. In many farms and commercial tree plantations, ants can positively influence the productivity of a crop or act as pests that can seriously damage farm output.

In coffee agroecosystems in Mexico, arboreal *Azteca* ants play an important role for coffee output in an unexpected and intricate way. *Azteca* ants build nests in ant-plant *Cecropia* trees, which are found intermittently in shade-grown coffee plantations where various tree species are planted with shade-loving coffee plants. Workers will descend from the

tree and forage honeydew from hemipteran scale insects (Chapter 5) that feed from the coffee plants. As scale insects are major pests of coffee plants, it would be reasonable to expect that this mutualistic arrangement with the ants—who maintain a healthy population of scale insects in exchange for the honeydew they rely on for food—would reduce coffee plant productivity. Indeed, the coffee plants near the *Cecropia* trees, where *Azteca* ants forage, do produce less coffee. But there is a twist: *Azya orbigera* Globe-marked Lady Beetle larvae eat scale insects as prey, and they can escape strong ant defenses by producing a special defensive substance that gums up ant mandibles. Adults of this beetle species, which do not produce the defensive substance and are thus chased away by the ants, are voracious predators of pest insects in the coffee plantation wherever there is not a *Cecropia* tree with its associated aggressive ants. By maintaining some localized populations of scale insects, *Azteca* ants also maintain a population of predacious beetles who in turn reduce the insect pest population across much of the plantation. The result is an overall increase in coffee plant productivity across the whole plantation even if there is a local reduction of coffee plant survival around individual *Cecropia* trees.

Ants can also be significant pests of agricultural crops. Sometimes, this pest behavior entails damaging the plants directly, as in the case of Leafcutter Ants in South America, Central America, and southern North America. This destruction is often swift and extensive, with some *Atta* colonies capable of entirely defoliating a fruit tree within just 24 hours. To avoid such a high economic cost, farmers utilize deterrent measures ranging from ant-specific insecticides to more creative approaches like sprinkling Leafcutter Ant

LEFT: In tropic forest ecosystems in the Americas, Leafcutter Ant foraging accounts for 25 percent of all herbivory and is a formidable threat to farms.

LEFT: Mealybug scale insects are a pest of coffee plants. A related species, the Green Scale insect, is tended by *Azteca* ants.

BELOW: Some *Azteca* ant species live inside the trunk of their mutualistic *Cecropia* host tree. They have also been observed healing wounded trees by patching up new holes.

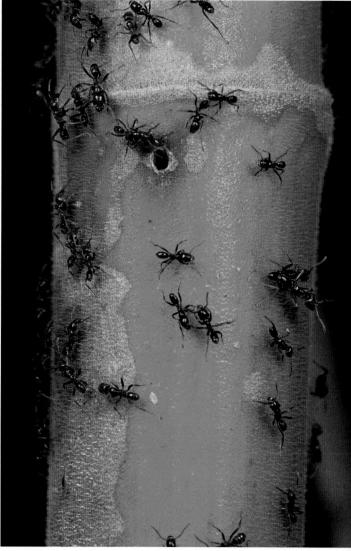

refuse onto crops to deceive foraging workers into believing that the crop leaves are unpalatable. The association of ants with sap-sucking insect pests, including defending the pests from predators like ladybugs, leads farmers (and gardeners) to commonly view most ants as pests. Furthermore, some very aggressive stinging species, like the Red Imported Fire Ant *Solenopsis invicta*, may attack people working on the farm or harass livestock grazing in a pasture.

However, certain predacious ant species, like *Oecophylla* Weaver Ants, can act as natural pest-control agents that reduce damage to crops. While Weaver Ants sometimes supplement their diet with honeydew produced by scale insects and related hemipterans, they primarily predate on other insects, including herbivores, and thus have a positive impact on crop productivity. Recognizing this benefit, farmers may move *Oecophylla* nests into commercial tree plantations to help suppress pest populations as biocontrol agents. Overall, whether ant species are beneficial or harmful to agricultural productivity varies depending upon the ant species and the context of the agroecosystem.

FOOD AND PHARMACEUTICALS

ANTS CAN IMPACT HUMAN FOOD production by promoting or undermining crop productivity, but they can also serve as a food source themselves. Dishes made with ants commonly include eggs or larvae, but adults (or parts of their bodies) are sometimes used as well. Various cultures view ant-derived cuisines as a delicacy, likely arising from their unique flavor and the difficulty of procuring enough ants to constitute a full meal. People may have originally turned to myrmecophagy (ant eating) for high-protein food supplementation, taking advantage of the high abundance of ants and their proximity to human communities.

Ant dishes are prepared from different ant species around the world. In modern-day Mexico, *escamoles* are ant larvae and pupae of two specific species of dolichoderine ant, the Velvety Tree Ant *Liometopum occidentale* and *L. apiculatum*. *Escamoles* are typically fried in butter and spices like chili and can be served solo or in a taco or tortilla shell. Preparation and consumption of *escamoles* dates to (and

surely predates) the time of the Aztec Empire, and are enjoyed by the Otomí and Aztec peoples to this day. On the other side of the world, in Southeast Asian countries such as Thailand and Cambodia, *Oecophylla* Weaver Ants have long been consumed in a similar manner. People in this region collect the larvae of Weaver Ants, the adults of which can be quite aggressive, by attaching baskets to long sticks and firmly beating near the arboreal nests, causing an abundance of larvae (and workers) to fall into the baskets. This haul is then cooked and eaten or sold at the market for a high price per pound, exceeding that of good-quality beef. Perhaps one of the most unique ant delicacies is *Melophorus* and

BELOW LEFT: *Camponotus inflatus* Honeypot Ant replete workers store food for their sisters, but they are also a sweet snack for people.

BELOW RIGHT: Called *escamoles* in Mexico, ant larvae are considered a delicacy in many parts of the world, fetching a high price per pound.

Camponotus Honeypot Ant replete workers, whose distended gasters filled with sweet liquid are collected and enjoyed by Aboriginal peoples of modern-day Australia.

People continue to find new ways to consume ants alongside more traditional forms of myrmecophagy. A distillery in the United Kingdom concocted a gin distilled with *Formica rufa* Red Wood Ants, which are said to give the "Anty Gin" a unique flavor deriving in part from the ants' formic acid content. On a similar theme, a small New York City brewer created a beer called "Funky Fresh" using yeast derived from live ants added during fermentation. A bar in Singapore came

RIGHT: A serving of prepared red ant chutney (*chapura*) for sale in India.

BELOW LEFT: A Thai soup with ant larvae.

BELOW RIGHT: A colorful French dish with lettuce, parsley, edible flowers, and *Polyrhachis* Spiny Ants.

up with a yogurt-based cocktail that is served topped with "black Thai ants" (likely *Polyrhachis*), and one particularly adventurous restaurant in Tokyo served up live shrimp with tiny black ants that are intended to give the dish an extra acidic kick. With a varied history spanning from thousands of years ago to the present day, people eating ants, in ways both old and new, is unlikely to fade anytime soon.

MEDICINAL APPLICATIONS

Several cultures also participate in a long tradition of consuming or otherwise using ants but for medicinal rather than nutritional purposes. One of the earliest documented references to ants is found in the fifth century BCE text *Sushruta Samhita*, a medical text attributed to the ancient Indian physician Sushruta. In this text, a diagnosis for what is believed to be diabetes—called *madhumeha*, or "honey urine"—includes observing that the urine of people with the

disease attracts ants and flies. In East Africa, the Maasai people, among others, traditionally utilize the vice-grip of powerful *Dorylus* Army Ant mandibles as emergency sutures, allowing the ants to bite down over wound openings and then cutting off the heads, locking the natural sutures in place. The 11th-century Persian historian Gardizi describes the use of "ant eggs and wolf's milk" among the Turkish people to cure a child ailment that was resistant to all other forms of medicine. Similarly, ants have for centuries been a part of traditional Chinese medicinal practice as a treatment for arthritis, among other health problems. The Spiny Ant species *Polyrhachis dives*, sometimes simply called the "black ant," is typically selected for this purpose due to its anti-inflammatory properties and consumed in powder form. A handful of studies have demonstrated potential anti-inflammatory properties and other medicinal benefits of *Polyrhachis dives* and *P. lamellidens*, including high vitamin and mineral content, and such investigations remain an active area of research. Some researchers are also pursuing antibiotic bacteria found in Leafcutter Ants as a possible source of antibiotics for people. While obviously only distantly related to humans, Leafcutter Ants create large and long-living subterranean nests that are not unlike dense human societies, both of which promote the spread of communicable diseases. These similar epidemiological conditions might have driven the evolution of antibiotic bacteria among ants that can be co-opted by humans to similar effect.

ABOVE: Ants are baked in bulk for use in traditional Chinese medicine, prescribed to relieve pain, increase longevity, and treat conditions such as asthma.

RIGHT: The powerful grip of *Dorylus* Driver Ants, also called Siafu, has been creatively co-opted by the Maasai people for use as emergency sutures.

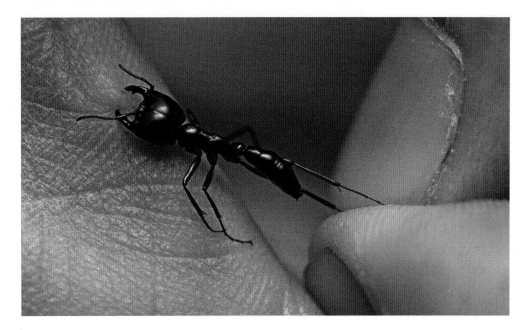

CULTURAL ICONS

ANTS ARE INCLUDED IN THE cultural traditions of people around the world. The mesmerizing similarity between ants and humans, along with the intriguing nature of visible eusocial behavior, may explain the frequent emergence of ants in human fables, parables, and myths. Cultural views of ants range from treating ants as teachers of humanity to considering the colonial insects an unenviable symbol of decay and destruction.

Ants can be seen as a source of wisdom for people, as suggested by the words of Benjamin Franklin in his 18th-century *Poor Richard's Almanack*: "None preaches better than the ant, and she says nothing." A relatively consistent

theme across cultures is references to the ant as a paragon of hard work, persistence, and preparation for the future. In one of the oldest documentations of this view, found in the Jewish text the Tanakh, Proverbs 6:6 instructs readers to "go to the ant, you sluggard; consider its ways and be wise!" Elsewhere in Proverbs, ants are again held up as an example of wisdom in that the insects may lack physical strength but still prepare food during the summer. The Greek storyteller Aesop includes as one of his fables a tale, *The Ant and the Grasshopper*, that carries a moral closely matching Proverbs:

LEFT: A 19th-century wood engraving depicting Aesop's fable, *The Ant and the Grasshopper*. In this rendition, the grasshopper begs from a hardworking society of ants.

endowed by nature with a strength much greater than my size so I might cope with the weight of a racism that crushes my spirit." Abraham Lincoln, prior to becoming the US President, supported his argument that slavery is manifestly morally unjustifiable by noting that even an ant "who has toiled and dragged a crumb to his nest, will furiously defend the fruit of his labor." And in Mexican culture, a proverb praises the busy work of the ant despite its small size and limited strength, claiming that "an ant on the move does more than a dozing ox," while a Chinese proverb extolls ant persistence with the reminder that "an ant may well destroy a whole dam." When great difficulties face people, people can look to ants for inspiration.

Myths arising in disparate regions across the world also feature ants as intimate associates of humans. In Greek mythology, Zeus transforms ants on the island of Aegina into men called "Myrmidons" over whom King Aeacus rules. Greek mythological tradition also includes a case of myrmomancy—divination through interpretation of ant behavior and appearance—in the story of King Midas, whose wealth is foretold by ants who, when the king was a child, dropped grains of wheat into the king's mouth while he slept. The Hopi people of North America have a legend where a race of "Ant People" saved them by protecting them in their subterranean tunnels during two ancient global cataclysms, one of fire and one of ice. And in the Popol Vuh, a recounting of Mayan mythology, Leafcutter Ants rescue the twin gods Hunahpú and Xbalanqué, who are faced as children with the intentionally impossible task of presenting four gourds filled with flowers from two specific species of plants to the Lords of Xibalba. When the Lords give strict orders to their guards to prevent the boys from accessing the flowers, they summon Leafcutter Ants, who proceed to avoid detection and secretly collect the flowers; thus, the twin gods prevail over the conniving Lords.

like the ants, it is best to prepare now for what you will need in the future rather than laze about in the present. Echoing this sentiment, the Roman poet Horace, in *Satires*, writes that "the tiny ant, a creature of great industry, drags with its mouth whatever it can, and adds it to the heap which she is piling up, not unaware nor careless of the future."

Cultural references to ants in proverbs and by notable figures sometimes favorably refer to the ability of a tiny ant to overcome significant challenges. Along these lines, a proverb of the Mossi people in modern-day Burkina Faso states that "when the ants unite their mouths, they can carry an elephant." South African singer and civil rights activist Miriam Makeba, in her book *Makeba: My Story*, writes: "I look at an ant and see myself: a native South African,

ARTISTIC INSPIRATION

WITH SUCH A CULTURAL FOOTPRINT among various peoples, ants have naturally found their way into many literary and artistic works. Poems that feature ants include those by notable historical figures like Richard Lovelace, Margaret Cavendish, and E. E. Cummings, as well as recipients of the Nobel Prize or Pulitzer Prize such as Robert Frost, Czesław Miłosz, Eugenio Montale, John Ashbery, and Maria Wisława Anna Szymborska. The use of ants sometimes comes across as playful, as in Szymborska's short poem "Four in the Morning" (1981):

> No one feels good at four in the morning.
> If ants feel good at four in the morning
> - three cheers for the ants. And let five o'clock come
> if we're to go on living.

Others take a more serious tone, such as Lovelace's 17th-century poem "The Ant," which uses the ant as a warning against spending all of one's time hard at work without appreciating the joys of life. One stanza is an apparent reference to Aesop's *The Ant and the Grasshopper*, decidedly coming out in favor of the grasshopper (or cricket):

JULY 2015
WWW.FB.COM/ANTMAN

LEFT: In his countryside anthill lair, the fictional Atom Ant enjoyed access to exercise equipment and a mainframe computer.

ABOVE: The 2015 feature film *Ant-Man* is based on the Marvel comic book superhero Ant-Man, who first debuted in 1962.

OPPOSITE: *Wryneck*, a 19th-century woodblock print, is an artistic rendering of a species of woodpecker hunting some ants walking along a tree trunk.

Cease, large example of wise thrift, awhile
(For thy example is become our law),
And teach thy frowns a seasonable smile:
So Cato sometimes the nak'd Florals saw.
And thou, almighty foe, lay by thy sting,
Whilst thy unpay'd musicians, crickets, sing.

Playfulness, seriousness, and even terror and horror all
emerge as themes in television shows and movie productions
that incorporate ants. The intrepid Atom Ant, a Hanna-
Barbera cartoon superhero that graced the small screen from
1965 to 1968, used the catchphrase "Up and at 'em, Atom
Ant!" Ants are a particular favorite of comedies on television,
found in episodes of *The Simpsons*, *Archer*, *Portlandia*, and
Letterkenny, among others. On the big screen, ants tend to be
associated with horror, including such early entries as *Them!*,
Phase IV, and *Empire of the Ants*. However, more recently
ants have been featured in a more positive light in films, with
Antz, *The Ant Bully*, and *Ant-Man* all taking an adventure-
comedy tone, while German director Werner Herzog's *Where
the Green Ants Dream* represents a work with serious intent
focusing on Indigenous land rights in Australia.

Ants in novels are sometimes used as extended metaphors,
as in Kurt Vonnegut's short story "The Petrified Ants" in *Look
at the Birdie*, a satirical critique of Soviet society through the
lens of two Russian ant paleontologists confronted with a
fossilized ant society that challenges their ideological
assumptions. In Toni Morrison's *Tar Baby*, the author
includes a long and poetic passage about the restricted life of
an ant queen that serves as an allegory about the suffocating
life of toil experienced by women in US society. And the
enemy race of "Formics" depicted in the *Ender's Game* series
is clearly based on ants (Formicidae). As the series progresses,
the destructive antagonism between humans and the ant-like
alien species is revealed to be based on a misunderstanding,
and the fictional human–Formic wars thus act as something

of a cautionary tale about the miscommunications and
xenophobia that drive many real wars between humans.

Artistic renderings of ants are included in the work of
12th-century French cleric Hugh of Fouilloy, titled *De Bestiis
et Aliis Rebus* ("Of Wild Animals and Other Things").
American writer Mark Twain's *A Tramp Abroad* includes a few
whimsical drawings of ants, each of which are given simple
descriptive titles like "Overcoming Obstacles," "Friends," and
"Prospecting." In the work of the Spanish surrealist artist
Salvador Dalí, ants typically represent death and decay, an
association that the artist attributed to a childhood
experience being horrified by ants swarming a half-alive
bat. Dalí might have been intrigued—or disturbed—to see
American artist Chris Trueman's 2010 piece *Self Portrait
With Gun*, which the artist uncannily created out of the
bodies of 200,000 real ants. A less destructive artistic use of
real ants is found in the 1989 installation *The World Flag Ant
Farm* by Japanese artist Yanagi Yukinori. Yukinori created a
giant ant farm using 182 chambers that each represent a
different world flag, representing the world as one
interconnected ant colony.

SCHOOL OF ANTS

HUMAN UNDERSTANDING ABOUT the functioning of ant societies can have a direct impact in several contexts. The remarkable ecological and behavioral diversity among ants allows for instruction in the classroom or through public programs about many different concepts in ecology and evolutionary biology, and the proximity of ants to human homes facilitates such engagement. Ants also inspire advances in engineering and programming.

Museums are often hubs of ant research as well as public outreach about ants. With thousands or even millions of ant specimens under curation, museums like the Field Museum in Chicago, the American Museum of Natural History in New York City, and the Smithsonian National Museum of Natural History in Washington, DC, historically support active myrmecological research while implementing programming and exhibits that communicate information about ants with the public. But sharing ant science more broadly extends beyond museums—with the rise of so-called "citizen science" or "community science," efforts to incorporate non-expert engagement into ant research have grown. The social network platform iNaturalist links formally trained biologists with community members around the world, facilitating the global collection and sharing of biodiversity information, including about ant diversity. The School of Ants, led by researchers at the University of Florida and North Carolina State University, was one of the larger community science programs and recently concluded after a decade-long run. This program provided a mailed kit and instructions for the simple collection of ants on the pavement and other common human-occupied habitats, and thousands of amateur collectors sent in ants from many locations. The researchers

BELOW LEFT: At the Citta dei Bambini ("City of Children") in Genoa, Italy, this child closely observes ants foraging for human food.

BELOW RIGHT: These ants were created by a British artist from recycled motorbike fuel tanks, for an installation at a street food market in London.

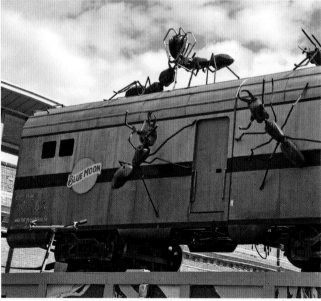

could then analyze the data and conduct research on, for example, the population genetics of the Pavement Ant *Tetramorium immigrans*. This program is an example of how ants can be used to educate people about the nature literally in their own backyard as well as advancing formal scientific knowledge about ants.

BIOMIMICRY

The collective behavior of ants is interesting on its own, but people have also discovered engineering and computer science applications based on the collective decision-making processes found in ants, an example of the broader practice of biomimicry. The "ant colony optimization algorithm" (ACO) is modeled after ant colonies, where simple rules by each "agent" (or "ant") in a simulation ultimately leads to an optimized decision that enhances efficiency. This algorithm was originally proposed as a new method to find an optimal path through a graph. While ACO algorithms may sound very

ABOVE: The Pavillon des Sciences ("Science Pavilion") in Montbéliard, France, features a giant sculpture of a *Formica* Wood Ant.

theoretical, they have been successfully applied in the real world to schedule delivery routes, develop telecommunication networks, and solve other logistical problems. Recent research has similarly looked to the bridge-building behavior of *Eciton burchellii* Army Ants, who form bridges out of their own bodies, for possible uses in the human engineering of self-assembling structures. The continuing technological development of "robotic ants," which began from observations of real-life ants, may lead to the use of "swarms" of individually small robots that can navigate through difficult terrain or collectively transport even very heavy objects. One advantage of this approach is called "fault tolerance," meaning that the process or task can properly continue even if one (or more) individual ant malfunctions.

CHANGE UNDERFOOT

IN THIS CURRENT HUMAN-DOMINATED geological age, the Anthropocene, humans have wrought massive global changes that impact all species, including ants, through radical transformations of habitats and climates. Some of these changes have resulted in an increased necessity to confront ants as troubling competitors and pests. Other impacts present severe challenges to the ants themselves, threatening their extinction through extreme ecological disruption. Observed shifts among ants can serve as warning signs to people about the extent of problems like habitat destruction and climate change.

Perhaps the most destructive human-caused (anthropogenic) change among ants is the spread of invasive species. According to the IUCN's Global Invasive Species Database, no fewer than 5 ant species make the list of the 100 worst invasive species in the world. These five ants of infamy are: the Yellow Crazy Ant *Anoplolepis gracilipes* (#6), the Argentine Ant *Linepithema humile* (#48), the Big-Headed Ant *Pheidole megacephala* (#68), the Red Imported Fire Ant

Solenopsis invicta (#86), and the Little Fire Ant *Wasmannia auropunctata* (#100). The ability of these species to greatly expand their geographic range likely involves some innate characteristics that afford these species a special resistance to disturbance and a great degree of behavioral flexibility. But humans have undoubtedly played a significant role, particularly in unintentionally facilitating the dispersal of ant colonies hitching a ride around the globe in cargo and passenger ships. Furthermore, anthropogenic climate change driven by the burning of fossil fuels, factory farming, and other human behaviors continues to raise global temperatures, which in turn allows some cold-intolerant invasive species to spread even further. For example, the Red Imported Fire Ant, a native of South America that cannot survive deep freezes, is believed to have been first established in the southern United States nearly 100 years ago. Over time, with increases in average annual temperatures, this species has expanded steadily northward and can today be found in US states as far north as Missouri and Virginia.

Invasive species significantly negatively impact human well-being as well as native ecosystems. The stings of swarming Fire Ants can render it quite unpleasant for people to spend time outdoors, and sting venom can even be life-threatening for those who exhibit strong allergic reactions to ant sting chemicals. Native ants, which have been shown to act as "ecosystem indicators" of habitat quality in regions such as Australia, can be entirely displaced by introduced invasive species. The Yellow Crazy Ant is so competitively dominant that it is even displacing the Red Imported Fire Ant in the southeastern United States. Such displacement raises the risk of extinction for native ant species that may already be under elevated stress from widespread anthropogenic habitat destruction, with negative effects throughout the local ecosystem for all animals (including people), plants, fungi, and even bacteria that have direct and indirect relationships with the native ants.

Besides invasive species, the general impact of climate change presents additional threats to ant diversity. Ants vary in their heat tolerance, and species with narrow ideal temperature ranges will be forced to relocate along with shifting climate. For ant species adapted to cooler temperatures or intolerant to very high temperatures, the only option is to move to higher elevations (up mountains) or higher latitudes (toward the poles)—as the globe warms further, even these last refuge regions may become intolerable, and thus many of these species will face extinction. Current human efforts to combat the pressures of invasive species and climate change include removal of established invasive species, the conservation of existing native habitat, and habitat restoration, but more large-scale programs are necessary, especially when it comes to reducing and reversing the effects of anthropogenic climate change. If people fail to come together locally, nationally, and internationally to address the many challenges facing ants, among other fauna and flora, then much of the fascinating and beautiful diversity detailed in this book could soon become a thing of the past.

OPPOSITE: *Solenopsis invicta* Red Imported Fire Ant mounds emerge along a curb after rain, as the colony moves toward the surface to avoid flooding in chambers deeper in the soil.

ABOVE: *Pheidole megacephala* Big-Headed Ant minor workers attempt to dismember a *Dorylus* Driver Ant forager.

GLOBAL BIG-HEADED ANT DISTRIBUTION

KEY

▪ Native

▪ Exotic: Non-native, likely dispersed by humans

▪ Indoor introduced: Non-native, found indoors but not (yet) in the wild

RIGHT: Human activities spread Big-Headed Ants around the world, extending their geographic range even to remote oceanic islands.

LINEPITHEMA

SUBFAMILY:	Dolichoderinae
DIVERSITY:	21 species
DISTRIBUTION:	Native: Central and South America and the Caribbean. Invasive: global.
HABITAT:	Forest, grassland, montane habitats
NEST:	Ground-nesting or arboreal
DIET:	Generalist scavengers and predators

Linepithema are small, monomorphic dolichoderine ants. They can be found in pristine or disturbed habitats nesting on the ground in soil, leaf litter, and under stones, or sometimes in trees.

ARGENTINE ANTS

Two of the 21 *Linepithema* species are considered invasive. The arboreal *L. iniquum* has spread globally but is limited to greenhouses. The same cannot be said of one of the worst invasive pest species in the world, the Argentine Ant *L. humile*. Naturally found in South America, it has invaded all Mediterranean or subtropical climates. Under climate change, it could spread even further into more temperate latitudes. It has devastating impacts on humans and the environment. It does not bite or sting but large numbers of ants will enter houses looking for food and water. It can displace local arthropods and tends plant-feeding insects like mealybugs and aphids that are crop pests.

Argentine Ants form supercolonies where many nests cover large areas and individuals do not exhibit aggression toward each other. Within Europe there are two Argentine Ant supercolonies. The main supercolony covers 3,700 mi (6,000 km) along the Atlantic and Mediterranean coasts, with a smaller supercolony in the northeastern part of Spain. Individuals from the same supercolony are never violent to each other even when collected from nests 3,700 mi apart. But if individuals from the two supercolonies meet, they are very hostile and will fight each other to the death.

DOLICHODERINE FEATURES

Linepithema have the typical appearance of dolichoderine ants, exhibiting a single, scale-like petiole node, smooth gaster, and lacking a sting or acidopore.

DORYLUS

Known as Driver Ants or Siafu, the winged males of *Dorylus* are called Sausage Flies. They excavate soil nests, moving up to 45 lb (20 kg) of soil every day in the first week of establishing a nest. Many species are generalist arthropod predators, with some termite or earthworm specialists. One pest species feeds on the below-ground parts of crops like sugarcane, coconut palm, citrus, and potatoes.

Up to 20 million workers live in a single Driver Ant colony. Unlike other doryline ants, they do not have defined statary or nomadic phases, with nest site emigration happening sporadically. A *Dorylus* queen mates between 15–20 times, storing 880 million spermatozoa to produce 3–4 million fertilized eggs per month.

FOOD OR FOE?

In a behavior known as "ant dipping," chimpanzees in Uganda feed on Driver Ants. They use a stick as a wand to safely dip for ants without being bitten. *Dorylus* ants are a major pest of honeybees in the tropics. They can destroy an entire apiary, carrying off all brood to be eaten within several hours. To prevent this, beekeepers in Ethiopia hang their beehives in trees with nests of highly aggressive and territorial *Crematogaster* ants. In three-quarters of direct encounters, *Dorylus quadratus* retreat from fighting with *Crematogaster chiarinii*. When conflicts do occur, mortality is always higher for *Dorylus* ants. A single *Crematogaster* colony can protect 100–200 beehives from Driver Ant raids.

SUBFAMILY:	Dorylinae
DIVERSITY:	61 species
DISTRIBUTION:	Sub-Saharan Africa and throughout Asia
HABITAT:	Grassland, savannah, woodland, forest
NEST:	Ground-nesting
DIET:	Generalist predators, some herbivorous species

WORKING BLIND

Dorylus ants do not have eyes, but this does not stop individuals like this soldier from defending the colony or catching prey.

LASIUS

SUBFAMILY:	Formicinae
DIVERSITY:	125 species
DISTRIBUTION:	Holarctic (Northern Hemisphere)
HABITAT:	Majority of habitat types in the region
NEST:	Ground-nesting. Some conspicuous mound-building species.
DIET:	Omnivores

Lasius are small to medium-sized ants found frequently in urban habitats. They are one of the most common ants in the regions where they are found. In Europe, *L. niger* and *L. flavus* are locally dominant; in the United States, it is *L. neoniger*. Most species are generalist omnivores, feeding on insect honeydew, nectar, and scavenged insect remains.

FLYING ANT DAY

In the Northern Hemisphere, many people will be familiar with the phenomenon of flying ant day. These are nuptial flights occurring in summer featuring the coordinated emergence of winged unfertilized queens with reproductive males from other nests for the purpose of mating. In the species *L. niger*, male aggregation syndrome occurs where extremely large numbers of males gather to mate with females. This synchronized appearance prevents inbreeding (mating with close relatives) and reduces the chance of predation.

A UK citizen science project asked people to record their flying ant day sightings. Over 13,000 responses were submitted, with 97 percent occurring in July and August. *L. niger* accounted for 88.5 percent of ants collected. Surprisingly, the flights were not timed simultaneously at a national or regional scale, although there was a general trend of flights occurring along a northward and westward gradient as summer progressed. Local weather conditions had the biggest impact on the timing of flights, with warm, non-windy weather required the day before as well as the day of the flights for the ants to emerge.

LONG LIVE THE QUEEN!
Unlike this worker, which may only live for a few months to a year, *Lasius niger* queens are able to live up to 29 years in laboratory conditions.

MELOPHORUS

Generally omnivorous, some *Melophorus* species will raid termite and Meat Ant nests, scavenge dead invertebrates, and feed on plant seeds. They are thermophilic (heat-loving) and are found in the hot, arid, and semi-arid regions of Australia. *Melophorus* ants mainly forage in summer and are active during the hottest part of the day, at temperatures between 98 °F (37 °C) and 129 °F (54 °C). They nest in soil and under rocks or wood. At night or if daytime temperatures are below 77 °F (25 °C), the nests are closed with sand or pebbles.

Melophorus belong to a wider category of Honeypot Ants, including *Myrmecocystus* in the USA and *Camponotus* in Australia. Honeypot Ants have a specialized worker caste, repletes, who act as a living larder for the colony. Repletes become swollen with liquid food stored in their distended gasters, which is provided to members of the colony through trophallaxis.

HONEY ANT MURAL

Melophorus repletes are often thought to be an Aboriginal food source but are not as commonly eaten as the highly prized *Camponotus inflatus* repletes. In 1971 the Papunya settlement in the Northern Territory of Australia was home to many different Aboriginal communities. Encouraged by a local art teacher, the senior men began painting their stories in a style known as "dot and circle," creating the Western Desert Art Movement. The first artwork they created was the *Honey Ant Mural*, which tells the Dreaming story of ants who later become men.

SUBFAMILY:	Formicinae
DIVERSITY:	91 species
DISTRIBUTION:	Australia
HABITAT:	Hot, arid, or semi-arid environments
NEST:	Ground-nesting
DIET:	Omnivores, some specialist predators and granivores

UNUSUAL MORPHOLOGY
Melophorus hirsutus have a number of unusual morphological features, including some individuals that have bulbous or projecting conical eyes.

MYRMECIA
Bulldog or Jack Jumper Ants

SUBFAMILY:	Myrmeciinae
DIVERSITY:	93 species
DISTRIBUTION:	Mainland Australia and Tasmania
HABITAT:	Forest, scrub, woodland
NEST:	Usually ground-nesting. Some arboreal.
DIET:	Omnivore

Myrmecia are medium to large ants identified by their large eyes and long, toothy jaws. Workers forage individually on trees near their nest site for tree sap, honeydew, or arthropods. Despite being very aggressive, some species engage in peaceful foraging. Ants share foraging trees even when individuals are from different nests and not related to each other.

DEADLY CREATURES

The confrontational attitude and excellent eyesight of Bulldog Ants mean they will stare down a human, possibly jumping at them. They have painful stings that can cause anaphylactic shock and death in allergic individuals. Between 1980 and 1999, six people died of *Myrmecia* stings, all within 20 minutes of a single sting. Ant venom immunotherapy is used as a preventive treatment on people allergic to *Myrmecia* stings. A small venom dose is given and gradually increased to alter the immune response.

SPECIES DISCOVERY

A type-species description uses an original individual specimen that a species name is then linked to. In the case of *Myrmecia*, the type species for the genus was collected from Botany Bay in 1770 by Joseph Banks while on the HMS *Endeavour* expedition with Captain James Cook. It was described to science by Johan Christian Fabricius five years later. The ant is now stored in the Natural History Museum, London. Another species, *M. banksi*, was described and named in 2015 to honor Joseph Banks.

FACIAL FEATURES
The distinctive many-toothed mandibles and large, visually acute eyes can be seen clearly in this *Myrmecia* worker ant.

TETRAMORIUM

Tetramorium are a diverse and successful group of myrmicine ants with a large geographic range occupying many habitats. While they are found throughout the Old World, the highest diversity of *Tetramorium* is concentrated in Africa, where there are at least 220 species.

PAVEMENT ANTS

A common urban ant in the USA is *Tetramorium immigrans*, the Pavement Ant. They form large colonies with potentially thousands of workers and are an invasive species originating from Turkey and surrounding regions. In the early nineteenth century, ships landing on the east coast transported Pavement Ants into the country, and they have now spread to at least 39 states.

In 2019 a study called the School of Ants used members of the public to collect ants and send them to scientists for DNA analysis. This study showed a lack of genetic variation in Pavement Ants, suggesting a single introduction event into the country or multiple events from a genetically similar group. There was also little genetic difference between invasive US and European ants. Their spread across the USA was likely assisted by humans from the initial site of introduction. They may owe their success to the lack of a similar ant as a competitor. They have general feeding habits as a scavenger and eat any plant or animal foodstuff discarded on sidewalks.

SUBFAMILY:	Myrmicinae
DIVERSITY:	586 species
DISTRIBUTION:	Diversity concentrated in the Afrotropics, but widespread in the Malagasy, Palearctic, Oriental, and Indo-Australian regions. Invasive species found in the Americas.
HABITAT:	Multiple: desert, savannah, grassland, woodland, forest, and urban habitats
NEST:	Ground, leaf litter, and arboreal
DIET:	Mostly predators, some granivores

MULTIPLE HABITATS
Tetramorium ants can nest and forage on the ground, in leaf litter, or on vegetation, including the forest canopy.

PARAPONERA
Bullet Ants

SUBFAMILY:	Paraponerinae
DIVERSITY:	Monotypic (one species)
DISTRIBUTION:	Neotropics
HABITAT:	Rainforest
NEST:	Ground-nesting, at the base of trees. Sometimes arboreal.
DIET:	Omnivores

Paraponera clavata, famously known as the Bullet Ant, is a very large black ponerine ant over ³/₄ in (2 cm) long. Feeding on a diet of invertebrates and plant parts, workers will carry extrafloral plant nectar back to the nest between their mandibles. Despite their aggressive reputation, Bullet Ants can peacefully coexist with other species. In Peru, colonies of the Stingless Bee *Partamona testacea* live with *Paraponera clavata* ants without any signs of apparent hostility. The bees benefit because they are not able to excavate their own nests, but there are no known benefits for the ants. Many parasitic insect species mimic the chemical profile of their hosts to avoid detection. This is not the case in the Stingless Bees, suggesting that the lack of aggression is a learned behavior by the ants.

THIS IS GOING TO HURT

The Schmidt Sting Pain Index rates the pain of insect stings on a scale of 1 to 4. A rating of 1 is a light pain and includes the sting of the Army Ant *Eciton burchellii*, while the medium pain of the *Dinoponera gigantea* ant sting is rated 2. In the case of the Florida Harvester Ant, *Pogonomyrmex badius*, a sting scores 3 and results in extreme pain lasting up to eight hours. The Bullet Ant sting scores a 4 and is said to be comparable to being shot. The pain is described as "immediate, excruciating pain and numbness."

ANTENNAL SCROBES

In addition to its large size, *Paraponera clavata* can be identified by the distinctive antennal scrobes, seen here as smooth polished troughs running above the eyes.

GLOSSARY

Acidopore

The circular opening at the tip of the gaster that can spray formic acid. A defining trait of ant species in the subfamily Formicinae.

Alate

A queen or male that is winged. Not all ant species produce alate queens and males.

Calyx

The part of an ant brain's mushroom body that transmits information, like that induced by olfactory signals, to the brain's mushroom body lobe regions.

Carton

A type of arboreal (tree) nest made from a mixture of animal excrement, plant material, soil, and ant excretions. Some species of *Polyrhachis*, *Dolichoderus*, *Crematogaster*, and other genera build carton nests.

Cephalothorax

The first body segment of spiders, consisting of a fused head and thorax. In ant-mimic spiders, the cephalothorax is modified to give the appearance of two body segments like the head and mesosoma in ants.

Claustral

A term used to describe queens that do not actively hunt for food to feed the first generation of workers. Instead, a claustral queen's enlarged wing muscles are metabolized and used to produce the first workers. By contrast, non-claustral queens actively hunt for food and typically do not have enlarged wing muscles.

Crop

This specialized structure stores food that can be regurgitated through oral-oral trophallaxis between workers and larvae, queens, or other workers. The collective set of crops among all workers in a colony is often called the "social stomach."

Cryptic

A descriptor for an ant species that is small and inconspicuously occupies leaf litter or soil. The term can also be used in evolutionary biology to describe a species that is genetically distinct from other species but hard to distinguish based on morphological traits alone.

Dealate

A queen that has lost her wings following mating, in preparation for colony foundation. Wing scars are clearly visible on the mesosoma of dealate queens.

Ergatoid

A reproductive ant (queen or male) that is permanently wingless. Ergatoid queens, which never had wings, are distinct from dealate queens that initially had wings that were subsequently removed.

Eusocial

Considered the most advanced form of sociality, eusocial societies are characterized by: (1) adult care for offspring other than their own; (2) overlapping generations within a colony; and (3) reproductive division of labor including an egg-laying queen and nonreproductive workers.

Extended phenotype

Traits among nonreproductive workers that increase the fitness of the queen. Worker traits like cuticular spines can be considered part of the queen's extended phenotype that enhances her reproductive fitness, even though the traits are present in another organism.

Formic acid

A chemical produced by ants and found in their venom, used for defensive and offensive purposes. English naturalist John Ray was the first to formally characterize formic acid, in 1671, by distilling a large number of ants.

Gamergate

A worker ant capable of storing sperm in a functional spermatheca and producing workers through sexual reproduction. Gamergates are rare and mostly confined to the subfamilies Ponerinae and Ectatomminae.

Gaster

The last body segment of ants, after the petiole (or postpetiole). Developmentally, the first segment of the gaster is the third (or fourth) segment of the abdomen.

Hemolymph

The insect equivalent of blood. Rather than a closed circulatory system like that found in vertebrates, the body cavity of ants is simply awash in hemolymph that remains in continuous direct contact with organs. This approach to oxygen transport is feasible for insects given their relatively small size.

Intercaste

Individuals in an ant society that are morphologically and functionally in between the worker caste and the reproductive caste.

Keystone mutualist

A species that engages in a mutualism with one or more other species which, if disrupted, would impact the entire local ecosystem. Australian *Rhytidoponera* species are considered keystone mutualists due to their plant seed dispersal behavior.

Life history strategy

The developmental processes deployed by an organism, from gamete through adulthood, especially those pertaining to fitness (reproductive success).

Maxillae

Mouthparts of an ant that are used to feel, smell, and manipulate food. Because they are softer than mandibles, maxillae are particularly important in handling soft or liquid food.

Mesosoma

The second main ant body segment, functionally similar to the thorax in other insects. In developmental terms, the thorax is fused to the first segment of the abdomen. For this reason, myrmecologists give a unique name to this body segment rather than calling it the thorax.

Metapleural gland

A gland, unique to ants, that secretes antibiotic fluid that collects in reservoirs on the propodeum. Some ant taxa, such as *Camponotus*, have evolutionarily lost the metapleural gland.

Mushroom body

A part of the ant brain that consists of the calyx and mushroom body lobes. It is associated with cognitive functions such as learning and memory.

Nanitic

A category of worker describing the first workers laid by the queen. Nanitics are usually smaller than subsequent workers and feed on eggs laid by the queen specifically as food for their consumption.

Ocelli

Three large simple eyes that form a triangular pattern at the top of the head of ant queens, males, and, rarely, workers. Ocelli are believed to aid ants in navigation.

Ommatidia

The facets that make up ant compound eyes. Ommatidia are relatively poor at producing good image resolution, but compound eyes are more sensitive to movements compared to the "simple" vertebrate eyes like those in humans.

Oviduct

The tube through which an egg passes from an ovary to the uterus. Lateral oviducts connect each ovary to a central oviduct that leads to the uterus.

Parameres

Part of the ant male reproductive organ. The outer parameres are used for grasping the queen during copulation.

Parthenogenesis

An asexual reproductive strategy found in a small number of ant species, in which reproductive females are produced through an unfertilized egg. In some parthenogenetic ant species, workers are genetic clones of the queen.

Penisvalvae

The innermost valves of the male ant genitalia. This serrated, blade-like structure is believed to act as an anchor during copulation.

Petiole
The "waist" segment between the mesosoma and the gaster, and developmentally the second segment of the abdomen. This feature is a defining trait of ants that distinguish the family from wasps and bees.

Phragmosis
A physical defense strategy whereby at least some workers have truncated body structures that are used to block the entrance to their nests, like the circular shield-like heads of soldiers in *Cephalotes* Turtle Ants.

Pilosity
Hairiness, or specifically the density of rigid hairs called setae. Setae are made from chitin, the same material that makes up the exoskeleton.

Postpetiole
The second waist segment in ant subfamilies with a subdivided petiole, including Myrmicinae and Pseudomyrmecinae.

Pronotum
The top (visible) plate of the first segment of the mesosoma.

Propodeum
The top (visible) plate of the last segment of the mesosoma. Developmentally, this is the first segment of the abdomen.

Replete
A specialized worker dedicated to the storage of food, like a living larder. The copious amounts of liquid food deposited inside repletes causes their gasters to become significantly distended.

Scape
The long first segment of an ant's antennae. The scape is connected to the funiculus, which is made up of multiple shorter segments. Together, the scape and funiculus form an elbowed joint that, along with the petiole and metapleural gland, represents a diagnostic trait of ants.

Sculpturation
The depressions and ridges of the cuticle. Sculpturation can be an important identifying feature that differentiates between ant species.

Spermatheca
A specialized structure that stores sperm. Throughout her life, an ant queen releases sperm from the spermatheca, one at a time, to lay fertilized eggs that will (typically) become workers.

Spiracle
A circular opening in the exoskeleton through which insects, including ants, uptake oxygen (breathe).

Trophallaxis
The direct transfer of fluids, often food, from one organism to another through regurgitation (oral-oral trophallaxis) or excretion (oral-anal trophallaxis). This process is facilitated through a muscular valve called the proventriculus.

Volsellae
The middle paired valves of the male ant genitalia, a structure unique to ants.

Workers
The nonreproductive caste in ants and other eusocial insects like bees and termites. Ant workers are always wingless. In a minority of species, workers have retained functional ovaries and can, when not repressed by queen pheromones or policing behavior by fellow workers, lay unfertilized eggs (which become males).

FURTHER READING

BOOKS

Ant (Reaktion Books, 2003),
Charlotte Sleigh

Ant Ecology (Oxford University Press,
2009), Lori Lach, Kristi Abbott, and
Catherine Parr (eds.)

The Ants (Springer, 1990), Bert
Hölldobler and Edward O. Wilson

Ants: The ultimate social insects
(Bloomsbury Wildlife, 2022),
Richard Jones

*The Ecology and Evolution of Ant-Plant
Interactions* (University of Chicago
Press, 2008), Victor Rico-Gray and
Paulo S. Oliveira

Exotic Ants: Biology, Impact, and Control
(CRC Press, 2021), David F. Williams

The Superorganism (W. W. Norton &
Company 2009), Bert Hölldobler and
Edward O. Wilson

REGIONAL/TAXONOMIC
GUIDES

GLOBAL
*Identification Guide to the Ant Genera
of the World* (Harvard University Press,
1994), Barry Bolton

EUROPE
*Ants of Britain and Europe,
A Photographic Guide* (Bloomsbury
Wildlife, 2019), Claude Lebas,
Christophe Galkowski, Rumsaïs
Blatrix, and Philippe Wegnez

*Ants (Naturalists' Handbooks):
24* (Pelagic Publishing, 2015),
Gary J. Skinner and Geoffrey W. Allen

The Ants of Central and Northern Europe
(Lutra, 2018), Bernhard Seifert

*The Ants of Poland with Reference
to the Myrmecofauna Of Europe*
(Museum and Institute of Zoology at
the Polish Academy of Sciences, 2012),
Wojciech Czechowski, Alexander G.
Radchenko, Wiesława Czechowska,
and Kari Vepsäläinen

Guide des fourmis de France
(BELIN, 2013), Thibaud Monnin,
Xavier Espadaler, Alain Lenoir,
and Christian Peeters

THE AMERICAS
The Ants of New Mexico
(Edwin Mellen Pr, 2002), Emma
Mackay and William P. Mackay

*Ants of North America:
A Guide to the Genera* (University
of California Press, 2007),
Stefan P. Cover and Brian L. Fisher

Hormigas de Colombia (Universidad
Nacional de Colombia, Universidad
del Magdalena, IAvH, Universidad
del Valle, 2019), Fernando Fernández,
Roberto J. Guerrero, and Thibaut
Dominique Delsinne

A Field Guide to the Ants of New England
(Yale University Press, 2012), Aaron
M. Ellison, Nicholas J. Gotelli, Elizabeth
J. Farnsworth, and Gary D. Alpert

*Guia para os Gêneros de Formigas do
Brasil* (Editora INPA, 2015), Fabricio
B. Baccaro, Rodrigo M. Feitosa,
Fernando Fernández, Itanna O.
Fernandes, Thiago J. Izzo, Jorge L. P.
de Souza, and Ricardo Solar

ASIA
Ants of Japan (Gakken, 2003)
Imai, H. T.; Kihara, A.; Kondoh, M.;
Kubota, M.; Kuribayashi, S.; Ogata, K.;
Onoyama, K.; Taylor, R. W.; Terayama,
M.; Tsukii, Y.; Yoshimura, M.; and
Ugawa, Y.

The Ants of Korea (Nature
and Ecology, 2017), Minsu Dong

AUSTRALASIA
*Australian Ants: Their Biology
and Identification* (CSIRO, 1999),
Steven O. Shattuck

Ants of New Zealand (Otago University
Press, 2008), Warwick Don

AFRICA AND MADAGASCAR

Ants of Africa and Madagascar:
A Guide to the Genera (University
of California Press, 2016),
Brian L. Fisher and Barry Bolton

Ants of Madagascar: A Guide to the
62 Genera (Association Vahatra in
Antananarivo, 2019), Brian L. Fisher
and Christian Peeters

Ants of Southern Africa, The Ant
Book for All (Slingsby Maps, 2017),
Peter Slingsby

MYRMECOLOGICAL SOCIETIES AND JOURNALS

Asian Myrmecology
www.asian-myrmecology.org

Insectes Sociaux
www.springer.com/journal/40/

International Network for the Study
of Asian Ants
www.antbase.net/anet/start.html

International Union for the Study
of Social Insects (IUSSI)
www.iussi.org

Myrmecological News
www.myrmecologicalnews.org

USEFUL WEBSITES

Alexander Wild photography
www.alexanderwild.com
A phenomenal visual record of ant
photography showcasing species
diversity and natural history

AntCat
www.antcat.org
A global catalog of ant names and
associated taxonomic literature

AntMaps/Global Ant Biodiversity
Informatics (GABI)
www.antmaps.org
An interactive page mapping ant
distribution according to different
levels of species taxonomy

AntWeb
www.antweb.org
An outstanding resource for those
interested in ants. Primarily based
on images and collection data from
museum specimen records. It is linked
to other sites such as AntCat, GBIF,
and AntWiki

AntWiki
www.antwiki.org
An online repository of information on
all aspects of ant biology maintained by
a global team of myrmecologists

Global Ants Database (GLAD)
globalants.org
A global database of ant abundance and
trait data for local assemblages compiled
from records of ant ecologists

Myrmecological News Blog
www.blog.myrmecologicalnews.org
An independent ant blog devoted
to myrmecology and related fields
with submissions from ant scientists
worldwide

INDEX

PICTURE CREDITS

The publisher would like to thank the following for permission to reproduce copyright material (l=left; r=right; t=top; b=bottom, m=middle):

1 kingma photos/Shutterstock; 2–3, 18bl, 18br, 20br, 21bl, 24, 25l, 25r, 28, 33, 38, 50, 52, 59r, 62, 63b, 66, 78, 82, 84tr, 85, 87t, 89t, 94, 97t, 98, 100, 101tl, 101br, 102, 105, 114, 124, 130b, 131t, 133, 134, 148, 150–151, 152, 154–155, 156, 157t, 158t, 161tl, 162bl, 163, 165, 168t, 168b, 170bl, 172, 183, 200, 201, 209 SR_001_Alex Wild; 4 supersaiyan3/Shutterstock; 6 Radu Bercan/Shutterstock; 7tl kajornyot wildlife photography/Shutterstock; 7br, 13ml, 13mr, 13bl, 44–45, 60l, 154tr, 161br, 205, 214 SR_010_Chien Lee; 9, 119, 144 Emanuele Biggi/naturepl.com; 13tl, 20bl, 61tl, 123, 132, 154tl, 189br, 190l, 202 Minden Pictures/Alamy Stock Photo; 13tr zaidi razak/Shutterstock; 13br Dirk Ercken/Shutterstock; 14–15, 19bl, 49tl, 49br, 59l, 69, 73, 95t, 140, 176 SR_015_Melvyn Yeo; 19tl, 37, 58l, 127t, 191br BIOSPHOTO/Alamy Stock Photo; 19br Francisco Lopez-Machado/Alamy Stock Photo; 30 Kidsada Manchinda/Shutterstock; 34, 63t, 84b, 166br SR_014_Nicky Bay; 41, 48 Martin Dohrn/naturepl.com; 42 AntWeb. Version 8.76.4. California Academy of Science, online at https://www.antweb.org. Accessed 11 March 2022/April Nobile/CASENT0423526_P; 51tr Redmond Durrell/Alamy Stock Photo; 51b Peter Yeeles/Shutterstock; 53tl epioxi/Shutterstock; 53br, 65b, 92 Nature Picture Library/Alamy Stock Photo; 55 Custom Life Science Images/Alamy Stock Photo; 54 NOAH PORITZ/SCIENCE PHOTO LIBRARY; 56–57 Worraket/Shutterstock; 57r SIMON SHIM/Shutterstock; 58r NICOLAS REUSENS/SCIENCE PHOTO LIBRARY; 60r, 61tr Mark Moffett/naturepl.com; 61br, 161bl Peter Yeeles/Alamy Stock Photo; 64 Vinícius Souza/Alamy Stock Photo; 65t dream_nantiya/Shutterstock; 70, 157b Clarence Holmes Wildlife/Alamy Stock Photo; 74 Prof. Bo WANG Director of Invertebrate Palaeontology Section; 77 AntWeb. Version 8.76.4. California Academy of Science, online at https://www.antweb.org. Accessed 1st March 2022/MichaelBranstetter/casent0106181_p_1_high; 80–81 SINCLAIR STAMMERS/SCIENCE PHOTO LIBRARY; 84tl, 162tr, 167 blickwinkel/Alamy Stock Photo; 86 Adobestock/David; 87b Andy Sands/naturepl.com; 88, 122 Ripan Biswas/naturepl.com; 89b Fehmiu Roffytavare/Shutterstock; 90, 139, 143 SR_011_Matt Bertone; 91 Anton Sorokin/Alamy Stock Photo; 93t, 126 SR_001_Alex Wild_Public Domain; 93b Leonardo Mercon/Shutterstock; 95b Frank Blackburn/Alamy Stock Photo; 96, 166tl Cherdchai Chaivimol/Shutterstock; 97b, 130t vinisouza128/500px/Getty Images; 99l Paul Souders/Getty Images; 99r Andrew Darrington/Alamy Stock Photo; 106 Ryszard Laskowski/Dreamstime.com; 109 Adobestock/Antrey; 110 Ijp2726/Dreamstime.com; 113 Patrick LORNE/Gamma-Rapho via Getty Images; 116–117 Irina Kozorog/Shutterstock; 118 MedioTuerto/Getty Images; 120 Radu Bercan/Alamy Stock Photo; 121l Dinodia Photos/Alamy Stock Photo; 121r, 153 Nick Upton/naturepl.com; 125 Khe1shoots/Shutterstock; 127b DR. JOHN BRACKENBURY/SCIENCE PHOTO LIBRARY; 128 Nick Vorobey/Shutterstock; 129t Kim Taylor/naturepl.com; 129b Charles Tee/Shutterstock; 135 Westend61 GmbH/Alamy Stock Photo; 136 Pavel Krasensky/Shutterstock; 147 Piotr Naskrecki/naturepl.com; 158b Kristian Bell/Shutterstock; 161tr Szasz-Fabian Jozsef/Shutterstock; 164bl Morley Read/Alamy Stock Photo; 164tr Juan Carlos Vindas/Getty Images; 166tr Hue Chee Kong/Shutterstock; 169l Alex Hyde/naturepl.com; 169r Stephen P. Yanoviak/Alamy Stock Photo; 170tr EyeEm/Alamy Stock Photo; 171 PhotoStock-Israel/Alamy Stock Photo; 175 wallaby/Shutterstock; 179 Adobestock/peter; 180 Christian Schroth/ullstein bild via Getty Images; 184 Narupon Nimpaiboon/Shutterstock; 186–187 Mauricio Palos/Bloomberg via Getty Images; 188 Klaus Mohr/Shutterstock; 189tl Nigel Cattlin/Alamy Stock Photo; 190r fitopardo/Getty Images; 191tr Lucy Calder/Alamy Stock Photo; 191bl Oxygensat/Shutterstock; 192 Marcus Harrison – food/Alamy Stock Photo; 193t THIERRY BERROD, MONA LISA PRODUCTION/SCIENCE PHOTO LIBRARY; 193b Avalon.red/Alamy Stock Photo; 194bl The Granger Collection/Alamy Stock Photo; 194–195tr Daniel A. Leifheit/Getty Images; 196bl Everett Collection Inc/Alamy Stock Photo; 196tr Marvel Studios/Walt Disney Studios/Kobal/Shutterstock; 197 Maidstone Museum and Art Gallery/Bridgeman Images; 198l CHRIS SATTLBERGER/SCIENCE PHOTO LIBRARY; 198r Dave Rushen/SOPA Images/LightRocket via Getty Images; 199 Hemis/Alamy Stock Photo; 206 Stephan Morris/Shutterstock; 210 Ken Griffiths/Shutterstock; 213 Pascal Guay/Shutterstock.

ACKNOWLEDGMENTS

It was only possible to write this book because of the diligent research of many myrmecologists around the world. The real credit goes to these scientists for uncovering the fascinating details of ant biology that are published here and to whom we are truly thankful for providing the scientific background to this volume.

We are equally indebted to the photographers whose work is featured in this book. Their skill at capturing the tiny world of ants brings the subject alive for all of us to enjoy. Many thanks to the myrmecologists of Twitter who were invaluable in highlighting important books for the resources section and include; Alice Laciny; Emeline Favreau; Brendon E. Boudinot; Gabi Camacho; Megan Wilson; Andrés Sánchez, Marek Borowiec, Roberto Keller, Adrian Richter, Mark Wong, and Anna Probert.

We are also grateful to Joanna Bentley, Anna Southgate, Myriam Birch, James Waters, and everyone else whose editorial work on behalf of Bright Press and Princeton University Press brought this book into being.

Benjamin would like to deeply thank those who provided him with love and support as he developed a love of ants: his parents, Scott and Judy; brothers, Joshua, Evan, and Jordan; PhD advisor, Corrie Moreau; Moreau AntLab friends including Shauna Price, Manuela Ramalho, Supriya, Peter Flynn, Jordan Greer, and Matthew Nelsen; grad school friends including Natalia Piland, Jackie Lungmus, and Laura Southcott; and numerous other lovely humans (you know who you are).

Heather would like to extend her gratitude to friends, family, and colleagues without whom the opportunity to pursue a life traveling the globe to study ants would not be possible. She is especially grateful to entomology colleagues at Harper Adams University for their ongoing support. It is to Daniel that she owes everything and so the biggest thanks go to him for his unwavering belief in her, as well as to Puzzles for providing the emotional support that only a cat knows how to give. Finally, this book is for Josh and the as yet unborn, unnamed baby Campbell-Miles. May your lives be filled with wonder, curiosity, and a love of insects.